American Inside Out Evolution

Workbook

Intermediate

SUE KAY
VAUGHAN JONES
PHILIP KERR

macmillan education

Macmillan Education

Companies and representatives throughout the world
American Inside Out Evolution. Workbook Intermediate

Adapted by Peter Magss and Catherine Smith / The Content Station team: Simon Campbell, George Wells, and Catherine Gray
Macmillan is a registered trademark.
First edition published 2017

ISBN: 978-607-473-630-4

Based on New American Inside Out Workbook Intermediate

Editorial Manager: Patricia Muradas
Editorial Operations Coordinator: Veronica Teodorov Ferreira
Editor: Cintia Zaitune
Concept design: Martha Tadaieski
Page make-up: The Content Station
Illustrations: Karen Ahlschläger pp6, 13, 22, 38; Gustavo Gialuca p10
Graphic Production: Kelly Gobbo
Photographic research: The Content Station
Cover concept and design: Jean Aranha
Cover photo: Svetlana195| Dreamstime | Dreamstime

The authors and publishers would like to thank the following for permission to reproduce their photographs:
Dreamstime / Canettistock p5(l), Dreamstime / Antonio Guillem p5(r), Dreamstime / Monkey Business Images p6, Dreamstime / Jorgenmac p8, Dreamstime / Bennn p11(a), Dreamstime / Jakub Gojda p11(b), Dreamstime / P0temkin p11(c), Dreamstime / Sven Bachstroem p11(d), Dreamstime / Kaspars Grinvalds p12, Dreamstime / Monkey Business Images p14, Dreamstime / Smileus p16, Dreamstime / Elena Nichizhenova p17(l), Dreamstime / Magspace p17(r), Dreamstime / Miguel Angel Morales Germo p19 (tl), Dreamstime / Ruth Lawton p19(bl), Dreamstime / Iakov Filimonov p19(tr), Dreamstime / Photographerlondon p20(l), Dreamstime / Borusikk p20(r), Dreamstime / Splosh p23, Dreamstime / Auremar p24(c), Dreamstime / Stangot p24(b), Dreamstime / Andrew282 p25, Dreamstime / Phanuwatn p28, Dreamstime / Vincent Giordano p29, Dreamstime / Niroworld p32, Dreamstime / Krystal Slagle p33, Dreamstime / Rosshelen p35, Dreamstime / Louis Davilla Wiyono p36, Dreamstime / Sbukley p37, Dreamstime / Jaguarps p39, Dreamstime / Elena Kazanskaya p40(l), Dreamstime / Lineartestpilot p40(r), Dreamstime / Monkey Business Images p43, Dreamstime / Arne9001 p44, Dreamstime / Viktoria Shvydkova p45(l), Dreamstime / Zdravinjo p45(r), Dreamstime / Jemastock p46(l), Dreamstime / Sharplaninac p46 (c), Dreamstime / Mheim301165 p46(r), Dreamstime / Viorel Sima p49, Dreamstime / Chesterf p50, Dreamstime / Fashionstock.com p51; iStock / alvarez p24.

CANIEM No. 2275

Macmillan Publishers S.A. de C.V. Insurgentes Sur 1886
Col. Florida, CP 01030
Álvaro Obregón
Ciudad de México
Tel: +52 (55) 5482 2200
elt@grupomacmillan.com

www.grupomacmillan.com www.macmillan.com.mx www.macmillanenglish.com

Printed in Brazil

This book was printed in January, 2025 by: Eskenazi Indústria Gráfica Ltda, Avenida Miguel Frias Vasconcelos, 1023 - Jaguaré - São Paulo - SP.

Contents

1 Friends

GRAMMAR

1 Find examples in the text of the tenses below.

I grew up in Canada, but I've been living in Mexico for about ten years. My wife is Mexican and I've known her for a long time. Before we came here, we were living in Montreal. We speak English at home. In the evenings, I'm learning Spanish.

Simple present

a is ____________________

b ____________________

Present progressive

c ____________________

Present perfect

d ____________________

Present perfect progressive

e ____________________

Simple past

f ____________________

g ____________________

Past progressive

h ____________________

2 Put the verbs in parentheses into the tense that is stated.

a *Simple present*
My best friend's name ___is___ (be) Roger.

b *Simple present*
I ________ (like) reggae and hip-hop music.

c *Present progressive*
I ________ (sit) at the desk in my room right now.

d *Present perfect*
I ________ (visit) the USA three times.

e *Present perfect progressive*
I ________ (live) in this town for eight years.

f *Simple past*
I ________ (go) to Brazil on vacation last year.

g *Past progressive*
I ________ (wear) jeans and a T-shirt yesterday.

3 Write questions that match the answers in Exercise 2.

a What is your best friend's name?

b What kind of ____________________

c Where ____________________

d How many times ____________________

e How long ____________________

f Where ____________________

g What ____________________

4 Write true answers to the questions in Exercise 3.

a ____________________

b ____________________

c ____________________

d ____________________

e ____________________

f ____________________

g ____________________

5 Complete with short answers.

a Is your best friend the same age as you?
No, he/she isn't.

b Is he/she from your town?
Yes, he/she ____________________.

c Were your parents' friends with his/her parents?
No, they ____________________.

d Is he/she studying English, too?
No, he/she ____________________.

e Has he/she been helping you with your homework?
Yes, he/she ____________________.

f Did you see him/her yesterday?
No, I ____________________.

g Was he/she working yesterday?
Yes, he/she ____________________.

h Have you ever been on vacation together?
No, we ____________________.

6 Write true short answers to the questions in Exercise 5 about your best friend.

a ____________________

b ____________________

c ____________________

d ____________________

e ____________________

f ____________________

g ____________________

h ____________________

7 Underline the correct verb form.

a Who **does live** / **lives** next door to you?

b What **do they do** / **they do** for a living?

c What kinds of movies **do you like** / **like you**?

d What **does make** / **makes** you sad?

e Which friends **do you see** / **see you** most often?

f Who **does know** / **knows** you best?

g Who **does send** / **sends** you the most text messages?

h What **do they write** / **write they** about?

8 Write true short answers to the questions in Exercise 7 about your best friend.

a ______
b ______
c ______
d ______
e ______
f ______
g ______
h ______

9 Correct the grammatical mistakes in four of the sentences below. Check (✓) the sentences that are correct.

a Fido and I usually get along very well together.
______
b We have never arguments.
______
c He always wakes me up in the morning.
______
d We normally go for a walk together in the afternoon.
______
e We enjoy often the same things.
______
f I buy him now and then clothes.
______
g I take him always on vacation with me.
______
h However, he's occasionally more interested in other women.
______

10 Write the words in order to make sentences.

a a am hurry I in usually .
I am usually in a hurry.
b buy ever hardly I online things .
______
c all friends I my text the time .
______
d do from housework I the time time to .
______
e a go I month once the theater to .
______
f am class English for I late rarely .
______
g about don't I often things worry .
______
h always dreams I my remember .
______
i alone be I often prefer to .
______

Change the sentences to make them true for you.

VOCABULARY

1 Complete the text with the phrases in the box.

a lot in common	always be there	click
close friends	drifted apart	fought
got along really well	~~hit it off~~	
our separate ways	ups and downs	

Charlotte and I first met when we were in college and we (1) *hit it off* immediately. We were at a party and we spent the whole evening laughing and talking. Very soon, we became (2) ______. We had the same interests and the same taste in music so we had (3) ______. We did a lot of things together and we (4) ______. At the time, I was dating a girl named Mandy from my hometown. But we didn't see each other often, and slowly we (5) ______. When we finally decided to go (6) ______, it was no surprise to our friends that Charlotte and I started dating. But our relationship changed and we didn't (7) ______ in the same way. "Everyone has their (8) ______," Charlotte said to me, but I knew something was wrong. We (9) ______ about little things and we finally broke up completely after one fight. I can't even remember what it was about. The funny thing is that we're now the best of friends and we have been for more than ten years. We know we'll (10) ______ for each other.

002 Listen and check.

2 **Match the questions (a–g) with the responses (1–7).**

a Do you have a lot in common with him/her?
b Are your close friends the same as his/hers?
c Did you hit it off immediately?
d Are there any times when you don't get along well?
e What kinds of things do you disagree about?
f Do you think you will drift apart or become closer as you get older?
g How sure are you that he/she will always be there for you?

1 No. At first, I didn't think she was interested in me at all. It was a long time before we clicked.
2 Not at all. She has her social life and I have mine.
3 One hundred percent. I believe that marriage is for life.
4 Politics. So we try not to talk about it.
5 We'll never go our separate ways. Every day, the love between us gets stronger.
6 Yes, we have our ups and downs. Especially when one of us is stressed.
7 In some ways, we're very different, but we share the same interests.

a	b	c	d	e	f	g
7						

3 **Write the missing letters to complete the conversation.**

a **Tim:** Hey, Joe! Hi! How's it (1) g o i n g?
b **Joe:** Not (2) b _ _. What (3) a _ _ _ _ you, Tim?
c **Tim:** Good. What are you (4) u _ to these days?
d **Joe:** Oh, not much, (5) t _ _ _ and that.
e **Tim:** We (6) s _ _ _ _ _ go out for a drink (7) s _ _ _ time.
f **Joe:** That (8) w _ _ _ _ be great. Look, I have to (9) r _ _. I'll give you a (10) c _ _ _.

003 **Listen and check.**

4 **Complete the conversation with the phrases in the box.**

better	keeping busy	pretty good
See you	~~things~~	up to

Nick: Hi, Sonya. How are (1) ___things___ going?
Sonya: Oh, (2) ______________. And you?
Nick: Yeah, fine. What have you been (3) ______________ lately?
Sonya: Oh, (4) ______________, you know. Work, work, work.
Nick: Yeah, me too.
Sonya: Good to hear it. Anyway, (5) ______________ get back to the office. (6) ______________!

004 **Listen and check.**

PRONUNCIATION

1 005 **Listen and check. Listen to the recording and practice saying the different sounds.**

/ɪ/	/i/
fill	feel
his	he's
live	leave
sit	seat
this	these
will	wheel

2 006 **Listen and check. Listen and write the words you hear.**

a ______________
b ______________
c ______________
d ______________
e ______________
f ______________

WRITING

Writing emails
Email vocabulary
Punctuation

inside out mail

My account | Sign out

Select	From	Subject	Date
Compose Mail	❐ **Zarina493@gmail.com**	**Hi, Philip.** How are things? I got yo	9:43 pm
Inbox (11)	❐ **sales@budgethotel.com**	**Confirmation** Thank you for your or	8:07 pm
Sent mail	❐ **delilmiernuir@mailbox.com**	**Vacations for $1**	6:55 pm
Drafts (2)	❐ **nicky.podolski@sky.net (2)**	**Next week** Good to hear from you	9:45 am
Spam	❐ **clancy.lindfield@elx.org**	**(no subject)** Give me a call when yo	9:28 am
Delete	❐ **b.wragg@fnebank**	**Loan request** Re: Account No. 017	9:01 am
Contacts	❐ **sonjakerr@telnet.net**	**FW: Vacation pictures** Got them thnx	Jul 22
	❐ **mrssuzy@yahoo.com**	**YOUR URGENT RESPONSE NEE**	Jul 22
	❐ **info@buyonline.net**	**Re: yr order ref no KY7342**	Jul 21
	❐ **kpjones21@jnet.com (2)**	**No problem** Just a quick note to sa	Jul 19
	❐ **joe.wilson@dudes.com**	**Dinner** Hi, Philip. See you on Friday	Jul 18

1 Look at the inbox of emails above. Which of these are probably:

a personal messages?
b business messages?
c spam?

2 Which hyperlink on the left or at the top of the email inbox do you click if you want to:

a read your emails? ___Inbox___
b end your email session? ________
c write an email? ________
d find a friend's email address? ________
e look at an email that you started writing but did not finish? ________
f report an email that you did not want to receive? ________
g send an email to the trash? ________

3 Match the punctuation marks to the words.

a	.	question mark
b	,	apostrophe
c	–	exclamation mark
d	?	comma
e	'	dash
f	!	period

4 Rewrite the email on the right, above using the punctuation marks in Exercise 3 and capital letters where necessary.

5 Read Katy and Paul's reply to the email in Exercise 4. Write Philip's reply.

FROM: phillip@mail.com
TO: katy@globalprovider.com
SUBJECT: Visit

Dear Katy and Paul
I havent written for a long time so I thought Id drop you a line are you on vacation now Im at the beach with my family but the weather is terrible rain rain rain I hope its better where you are let me know how things are going I hope youre well
Best wishes
Philip
PS A friend of mine is going to be in Chicago next month he doesnt know anyone there is there any chance you could show him around for one day Id be really grateful

FROM: katy@globalprovider.com
TO: phillip@mail.com
SUBJECT: RE: Visit

Hi Philip,
Just a quick note to say yes – no problem. We'd be really happy to show your friend around when he comes to Chicago. Can you tell us a little more about him? What's his name? What kinds of things does he like to do? When's he coming? Has he been here before?
Love,
Katy & Paul
P.S. Could you send us a picture of him?

2 Adrenalin

GRAMMAR

1 **Write the words in order to make sentences.**

a a horse I many ridden 've times .
I've ridden a horse many times.

b a I in never river swum 've .
______

c been have I India n't to yet .
______

d already done homework I my 've .
______

e ages anyone for have I met n't .
______

f eaten yet I have lunch n't .
______

g have lately much I n't slept .
______

Change the sentences to make them true for you.

2 **Use the prompts to write questions.**

a you / ever / have / X-ray?
Have you ever had an X-ray?

b you / ever / play / badminton?
______

c you / ever / climb / mountain?
______

d you / ever / meet / Australian?
______

e you / ever / fly / in / helicopter?
______

f you / ever / sleep / on / beach?
______

Write true answers to the questions.

3 **Put the verbs in parentheses into the simple past or the present perfect.**

A: (1) *Have you ever been* (you ever be) really scared?
B: Yes, I have. One day last week, I (2) ______ (be) really terrified.
A: Why? What (3) ______ (happen)?
B: I (4) ______ (see) a wasp. It was enormous. I (5) ______ (never see) one like that before.
A: (6) ______ (you kill) it?
B: Certainly not.
A: (7) ______ (you always be) scared of wasps?
B: Yes, but I (8) ______ (be) a lot more scared of them since one stung me recently.

007 **Listen and check.**

4 **Correct the mistakes in the questions.**

a What you were doing at 9:00 p.m. last Saturday?
What were you doing at 9:00 p.m. last Saturday?

b What did you wearing?
______

c How were you feel?
______

d What you did after that?
______

e What time went you to bed?
______

f When you got up the next day?
______

Write true answers to the questions.

a ______
b ______
c ______
d ______
e ______
f ______

5 **Put the verbs in parentheses into the simple past or the past progressive.**

One day, Leo (1) *was walking* (walk) home from work. The sun (2) ______ (shine) and he (3) ______ (feel) happy. Suddenly, he (4) ______ (see) a group of people who (5) ______ (look) up at the top of a building. Leo (6) ______ (look) up, too. A woman (7) ______ (stand) on the roof of the building. Then, the woman (8) ______ (jump). Leo's heart (9) ______ (stop), but then, after a second or two, her parachute (10) ______ (open).

6 Put the adjectives in parentheses into the comparative or superlative form. Insert *than* and *the* where necessary.

a My friends are funnier than (funny) me.
b I'm ______________ (lucky) person that I know.
c I feel ______________ (relaxed) today than yesterday.
d My kitchen is ______________ (cold) place in the house.
e My sister is ______________ (pretty) girl in the world.
f I find history ______________ (interesting) sports.
g ______________ (sad) movie I've ever seen is *The Fault in Our Stars*.
h I'm usually ______________ (happy) my best friend.

Change the sentences to make them true for you.

7 Underline the correct alternative.

a Scuba diving in the Bahamas was **by far** / **slightly** the most exciting thing I've ever done.
b It was **by far** / **much** easier than I thought.
c The Bahamas are **a lot** / **just as** good for diving as the Red Sea.
d The hotels are **by far** / **slightly** more expensive than in my country.
e The weather is **a lot** / **by far** hotter in the summer.
f My last vacation wasn't **a bit** / **nearly** as nice as this.

8 Rewrite the sentences, beginning with the words given.

a Tennis is more popular than badminton.
Badminton isn't as popular as tennis.
b Bungee jumping isn't as difficult as kite surfing.
Kite surfing is ______________.
c La Bombonera Stadium in Buenos Aires is not as big as the Macaranã Stadium in Rio.
The Maracanã Stadium in Rio is ______________.
d The Red Sox are better than the Cubs.
The Cubs aren't ______________.
e Baseball isn't nearly as exciting as soccer.
Soccer is a lot ______________.
f Snowboarding is much more fashionable than fishing.
Fishing isn't ______________.
g Horseback riding isn't as dangerous as boxing.
Boxing is ______________.

VOCABULARY

1 Insert the missing letters in the non-gradable adjectives and match them with the gradable adjectives in the box.

angry	cold	funny	good
~~pretty~~	scared	surprised	tired

a g_rg_ _ _s pretty
b _xh _ _ st_d ______
c h_l_r_ _ _s ______
d f_r_ _ _s ______
e t_rr_f_ _d ______
f _st_n_sh_d ______
g _ncr_d_bl_ ______
h fr_ _z_ng ______

2 Complete the sentences with the words in the box.

bored	embarrassed	nervous
scared	~~thrilled~~	worried

a I was absolutely thrilled – it was a fantastic gift, thank you.
b I was extremely ______________ – the man had a gun.
c I was feeling fairly ______________ – it was only my second driving lesson.
d I was so ______________ – I almost fell asleep.
e I was very ______________ about you – I didn't know you were going to be late.
f I've never been so ______________ in my life – my face turned bright red.

3 Circle the 13 sports in the wordsquare. The first one has been done for you.

basketball	ping pong	skiing
windsurfing	~~baseball~~	boxing
badminton	golf	karate
judo	ice hockey	fishing
cycling		

W	B	A	S	E	B	A	L	L	C	E	C
O	I	B	B	P	I	N	G	P	O	N	G
C	M	N	A	A	E	B	J	Q	J	B	O
Q	Y	F	D	S	D	G	O	U	B	D	P
C	G	C	I	S	K	M	I	X	D	G	V
X	S	O	L	S	U	E	I	D	I	O	V
S	Z	I	L	I	H	R	T	N	L	N	X
M	C	D	B	F	N	I	F	B	T	N	G
Z	D	T	Z	N	P	G	N	I	A	O	A
T	K	A	R	A	T	E	R	G	N	L	N
L	J	B	U	S	K	I	I	N	G	G	L
I	C	E	H	O	C	K	E	Y	Y	A	L

4 Which 9 sports from the wordsquare in Exercise 3 use equipment you can see in the store window?

1 basketball
2 ______
3 ______
4 ______
5 ______
6 ______
7 ______
8 ______
9 ______

5 Complete the sentences with the words in the box.

board	harness	kite	rope
shoes	waterproof	~~wetsuit~~	

a The water was very cold so we needed a wetsuit.
b The cliffs were high, but we came down in a ______.
c Some surfers spend more than $650 on their most important piece of equipment – their ______.
d Near the top of the mountain, the climbers used a ______ for extra safety.
e Many children enjoy flying a ______.
f Cyclists need ______ clothes in wet countries like Ireland.
g One famous French climber does not use climbing ______.

6 Match the sentence beginnings (a–h) with their endings (1–8).

a Make sure that you drink lots of water
b I have a painful black eye
c I'm wearing sandals
d You should have an X-ray
e My finger's killing me
f Keep the skin clean
g She twisted her ankle
h I often get a cramp

1 and cover it with a Band-Aid.
2 and found it hard to walk.
3 because I have a blister on my toe.
4 so that you don't get dehydrated.
5 to see if your thumb is broken.
6 when I run for more than five minutes.
7 where he hit me.
8 where the bee stung it.

a	b	c	d	e	f	g	h
4							

7 Underline the correct alternative.

a You'd better see a dentist about that **dehydrated** / **loose** tooth.
b You need to get to a hospital for an **ankle** / **X-ray**.
c You really should put some **lotion** / **thumb** on the sunburn.
d You'd better take a rest if you're **limping** / **twisted**.
e You need to find out why your **tooth** / **wrist** is swollen.
f You really should take some aspirin for your **headache** / **red nose**.
g You'd better put a **cramp** / **Band-Aid** on that to keep it clean.
h You need to change shoes to stop the **blisters** / **sandals**.

PRONUNCIATION

1 Look at the auxiliary verbs (*was*, *were*, *has*, *have*) in the following conversations. Which verb is pronounced in the strong form and which is weak?

1 A: I was thinking of going skydiving. weak
B: Were you?

2 A: We were beginning to feel nervous.
B: I wasn't!

3 A: She has never been so surprised.
B: Well, I have!

4 A: Have you ever ridden a horse?
B: No, but my wife has.

5 A: Were you thinking about me?
B: Yes, I was.

	strong	weak
was	/wɑz/	/wəz/
were	/wɜr/	/wər/
has	/hæz/	/həz/
have	/hæv/	/həv/

008 Listen and check. Practice saying the sentences.

LISTENING

1 009 **Cover the listening script and listen to four people talking about the most exciting vacations they have ever had. Match the speakers with the pictures.**

a Speaker 1 picture _____
b Speaker 2 picture _____
c Speaker 3 picture _____
d Speaker 4 picture _____

2 Listen again. Are the sentences true (T) or false (F)?

Speaker 1
a They had to use special equipment. _____
b The sharks suddenly attacked. _____
Speaker 2
c They went flying every day. _____
d One plane collided with another plane. _____
Speaker 3
e They spent a week in the submarine. _____
f They used lights to help them see under the water. _____
Speaker 4
g They were looking for elephants. _____
h They spent the nights with the local people. _____

3 Look at the script. Explain what *it* refers to.

a I didn't really believe *it* (*Speaker 1*)
that it was possible to swim with sharks.
b *It* was amazing (*Speaker 1*)
_____
c you have to try to shoot *it* down (*Speaker 2*)
_____
d *It* was a lot of fun (*Speaker 2*)
_____
e *it* took us under the ice (*Speaker 3*)
_____
f *it* was really beautiful (*Speaker 3*)
_____
g the end of *it* all (*Speaker 4*)
_____

1 I was on vacation once in the Bahamas, and I saw an advertisement for an excursion – "Swim with Sharks," it said. I didn't really believe it, but I thought it was a fascinating idea, and two days later I decided to give it a try. I was with a group of about 20 other people on a special boat. We all put on our diving equipment. It was made of a special material, something very strong, to protect us against the sharks. The sharks arrived and, at first, I was absolutely terrified, but they were really friendly. They only wanted to play! It was amazing.

2 The most exciting thing I've ever done was just over a year ago when I was in Canada. I spent a week there, and every afternoon we went up in a Harvard jet, and what happens is, you fly around looking for other jets, and when you see one, you have to try to shoot it down. There's a sort of gun, a sort of laser, and when you hit another jet, you hear a loud noise and you can see black smoke. In one week, I shot seven other planes. It was a lot of fun, but it was really expensive and I could never afford to do it again.

3 A few years ago, I spend a week in the Canadian Arctic with a friend of mine. One day we went out in a small submarine and it took us under the ice. It was totally dark, but we had big lights, and they lit everything up, so we could see, you know. There were some really strange fish, and one time I saw something that looked like a shark, but I'm not sure it was one. Then we arrived at an old shipwreck, an old ship from the seventeenth century. I don't know why, but I was a little scared for some reason. It was really beautiful, though.

4 Last year, I went to see my friend Clyde, who lives near Chiang Mai in the north of Thailand. Near where he lives, there's an elephant camp, and we booked a three-day trip, you know, a trek, a sort of safari, and we spent three days on the back of the elephants, and at night, we stayed in little villages with the mountain people. At the end of it all, I was filthy and exhausted; but what a trip! And the people that we met were all so incredibly nice.

3 Relationships

GRAMMAR

1 **In each sentence, put one verb into the simple present and the other into the present progressive.**

a I ___am smiling___ (smile) because you ___remind___ (remind) me of someone.

b We ______________ (share) a room, but we ______________ (not have) much in common.

c I ______________ (know) that you ______________ (laugh) at me.

d I ______________ (look) for someone who ______________ (believe) in the same things as me.

e I ______________ (admire) the way she ______________ (try) to do well now.

f I ______________ (not understand) why you ______________ (cry).

g I ______________ (read) a book that I really ______________ (like).

h I ______________ (hate) the job that I ______________ (do) right now.

2 **Complete the conversations with the verbs in the box in the simple present or the present progressive.**

have	look	think

a A: How long have you had your car? It ___looks___ very old.
B: Yes, it is. I ______________ of getting a new one.

b A: John, hi. It's Mom. ______________ (you) time to talk?
B: I can't talk now. I ______________ dinner with my girlfriend.

c A: Why ______________ (you) at me like that?
B: It's because you ______________ tomato sauce on your nose!

d A: What ______________ (you) of the new James Bond movie?
B: I don't know yet. I ______________ of going to see it this evening.

3 **Complete the sentences with *for* or *since*.**

a I've been drinking coffee ___since___ *I was fourteen*.

b I've been to the movies only once ______________ *last summer*.

c I've been using the internet ______________ *years and years*.

d I've been wearing this perfume ______________ *last year*.

e I've eaten nothing ______________ *eight o'clock this morning*.

f I've had the same group of friends ______________ *we were in high school*.

g I haven't read anything interesting ______________ *four or five months*.

h I've wanted to make a change in my life ______________ *a long time*.

Make the verbs negative or change the words in italics to make the sentences true for you.

4 **Put the verbs in parentheses into the present perfect progressive.**

Carol is single, but she (1) ___'s been looking___ (look) for a boyfriend. She (2) ______________ (go) to online dating sites and she (3) ______________ (write) to one guy for a few months. She (4) ______________ (dream) of finding the ideal guy and she (5) ______________ (hope) she'll find him soon. Her friends (6) ______________ (tell) her to be more realistic. They (7) ______________ (try) to stop her from being so romantic, but she (8) ______________ (not listen).

5 Put the verbs in parentheses into the simple or progressive form of the present perfect. Then answer the questions.

a How long ___have you known___ (you know) your best friend?

b How long ______________ (you learn) English?

c How long ______________ (you sit) in the same chair?

d How long ______________ (you have) your smartphone?

e How long ______________ (you be) with your boyfriend/girlfriend?

f How long ______________ (you like) your favorite singer or band?

g How long ______________ (you wear) the shoes that you have on?

h How long ______________ (you do) this exercise?

Write true answers to the questions.

VOCABULARY

1 Complete the sentences with an appropriate family word.

a I used to be married to him. He's my ___ex-husband___.

b We have the same mother, but different fathers. She's my ______________.

c He's my brother's son. He's my ______________.

d We've been dating for two years. He's my ______________.

e He married my mother after my father died. He's my ______________.

f She married my son. She's my ______________.

g I don't have any brothers or sisters. I'm an ______________.

h She's my brother's daughter. She's my ______________.

2 Write the words in order to complete the questions. Then answer the questions.

a at fallen first in love sight ?
Have you ever ___fallen in love at first sight___?
____

b an been dating online site to ?
Have you ever ______________?
____

c dreams meet of person the your ?
Do you think you will ever ______________?
____

d ever proposed someone to ?
Have you ______________?
____

c had have relationships serious you ?
How many ______________?
____

3 Match the words in the box with the sentences (a–h)

considerate	easygoing	generous	shy
optimistic	reliable	~~sociable~~	witty

a I think that I'm a very friendly person and I like being with other people. ___sociable___

b I find it difficult to talk to other people, especially people that I do not know. ______________

c I'm very positive about life and I think that most things are usually OK in the end. ______________

d I always think about other people's feelings. ______________

e I say a lot of funny things and people laugh when they are with me. ______________

f I'm always happy to give my time or my money to people who need it. ______________

g I always do what I say I will do and my friends know that I will always help them. ______________

h I'm happy to do what other people want, even if I don't agree with them. ______________

4 Complete the conversation with the words in the box.

big-headed	~~cheerful~~	demanding
faithful	realistic	self-centered

A: What's the matter, John? You're usually so (1) ___cheerful___.

B: It's Helen. She's so (2) ______________. She wants me to be with her twenty-four hours a day!

A: So? That's good, isn't it?

B: No! We always have to do exactly what she wants. She's completely (3) ______________.
And everything that she does, she thinks she's the best. I've never known anyone so (4) ______________.

A: But at least she's (5) ______________. She never even looks at other men. Anyway, if you're so unhappy, why don't you split up?

B: Why? Because I have to be (6) ______________.
I know I won't find anyone else who wants to date me.

010 Listen and check.

5 Match the sentences (a–h) with the responses (1–8).

a She talks a lot, doesn't she?
b He seemed a little young, don't you think?
c She's not at all bad-looking, is she?
d He's really confident, isn't he?
e She didn't seem very interesting to me.
f He was a little mean, wasn't he?
g It's really difficult to talk to her, isn't it?
h He's not exactly talkative, is he?

1 I agree. She tends to be a little boring.
2 No, he's very quiet today.
3 No, she's very good-looking, in my opinion.
4 Well, he wasn't particularly old, that's for sure.
5 Yes, he's very self-centered.
6 Yes, he was absolutely awful.
7 Yes, she certainly tends to dominate the conversation.
8 Yes, there are times when she can be impossible!

a	b	c	d	e	f	g	h
7							

6 Complete the conversation. The first letter of each word has been given for you.

a **A:** I'm sorry I said that to her. I know I (1) c<u>an</u>__________ be a little thoughtless at times.
b **B:** You weren't very (2) c__________!
c **A:** I know. But when I'm tired I (3) t__________ to say the first thing that comes into my head.
d **B:** Well, try to be a (4) l__________ more sensitive next time, OK?
e **A:** OK. But she wasn't (5) e__________ tolerant herself, was she?
f **B:** True. She's not (6) v__________ broad-minded, but I think she was just tired.
g **A:** Yes, I (7) g__________ so. We can all be a little difficult when we're tired.

011 Listen and check.

PRONUNCIATION

1 012 Listen to the words in the box. Is the <u>underlined</u> sound /θ/ or /ð/? Put the words in the correct column.

~~ano<u>th</u>er~~	~~a<u>th</u>letic~~	bo<u>th</u>	fai<u>th</u>ful
fa<u>th</u>er	mara<u>th</u>on	some<u>th</u>ing	<u>th</u>ere
<u>th</u>ink	<u>th</u>is	<u>th</u>ose	<u>th</u>oughtful
toge<u>th</u>er	wea<u>th</u>er		

/θ/	/ð/
athletic	another

013 Listen and check. Repeat the words.

2 Look at the personal advertisement. <u>Underline</u> the words that contain the /θ/ sound. Circle the words that contain the /ð/ sound.

> **HEALTHY** thirty-something theater fan looking for someone with that special something. Call me earlier than the third Thursday of this month. They call me Arthur!

014 Listen and check.

3 015 Try saying the sentences below. Then listen and repeat them.

a They think that there'll be wet weather this month.
b My father thought that my brother threw the ball.
c This is the third thing we've seen at this theater.

WRITING

Writing an informal email
Linking sentences with *anyway*

1 **Read the email. Is it (a) a romantic email or (b) an email from one friend to another?**

FROM: chiyo@mail.com

TO: vince@globalprovider.com

SUBJECT: **RE: Visit**

1 Hi Vince,

2 Thanks for your email. It was great to hear from you again. I'm sorry I didn't reply sooner. I've been meaning to get in touch, but you know how it is. Anyway, hope that you're well and that everything is going well with your studies. How is everybody in college?

3 I really enjoyed my time in the USA, but I missed my friends back in Japan. I was happy to get back here and to see everyone again. Do you remember Masako? We often talk about you, and she sends her love. I've had some emails from some of our friends in the USA. Do you still see them?

4 I've been looking for a job, but I haven't had much luck. So I've decided to come back to the USA for a few months. My father said that one of his contacts was looking for someone who speaks English and Japanese. I have an interview with the company in two weeks. I can't wait!

5 Do you still have the same phone number? I'll give you a call when I arrive. Maybe we could go out for dinner.
It would be great to meet up again.

6 Love,
Chiyo

7 P.S. I still have your umbrella!

2 **Read the email again and match the headings below with the parts of the email.**

a the closing phrase 6

b news about friends ____

c introduction and apologies ____

d the opening phrase ____

e news about her life ____

f arranging to meet ____

g anything the writer forgot to mention earlier (postscript) ____

3 **Find informal phrases in the email that match the more formal phrases below.**

a I am really looking forward to it.

____

b I look forward to seeing you again.

____

c I was delighted to read your news.

____

d I will telephone you.

____

e It was my intention to write.

____

f Please accept my apologies for not replying before.

____

g Yours sincerely,

____

h She sends her regards.

____

4 **Why does the writer use the word *anyway* in the first paragraph?**

a to say that something is important

b to say something that the writer forgot

c to change the subject

5 **Insert *anyway* in an appropriate place in the short paragraphs below.**

a I haven't been doing much recently. It's been very quiet at college. I have to go now and buy some milk before the store closes.

b It was good to hear from you. I hope you'll tell me more in your next email. The reason I'm writing now is to tell you my big news. I'm getting married!

c Mike and Marion split up. He's feeling miserable and she met another guy. What have you been doing in the last few weeks?

6 **Imagine that you are Vince and write a reply to Chiyo. In your email, include the following points:**

- thanks for her email
- news about friends
- news about what you are doing now
- looking forward to seeing her

4 Party

GRAMMAR

1 Delete the words *it* or *them* in four of the sentences below. Check (✓) the sentences that are correct.

a He had a hat, but he didn't put it on.
b Some people were dancing, and they asked us to join them in.
c The festival goes it on for four days.
d The fireworks went off them at midnight.
e The house burned it down in an enormous fire.
f The children are very young and someone has to take care of them.
g We have a lot of work to do and we need to get down to it.

2 Replace the words in italics with *it* or *them*. Sometimes you will need to change the word order of the sentence.

a I enjoy taking care of *children*.
I enjoy taking care of them.
b I always wear out *my shoes* very quickly.
____
c I like trying on *clothes* at the mall.
____
d I'm really looking forward to *my summer vacation*.
____
e It takes me a long time to get over an *illness*.
____
f People often ask me to turn down *my music*.
____
g I find it difficult to come up with *good ideas*.
____
h I never look up *new words* in a dictionary.
____

Check (✓) the sentences that are true for you.

3 Put the verbs in parentheses into the *-ing* form or the *to*-infinitive.

a Are you doing (do) anything interesting this evening?
b Are you __________ (go) to any parties in the next few weeks?
c Are you __________ (meet) anyone later today?
d Are you going __________ (use) public transportation this week?
e Are you going __________ (watch) TV later today?
f What time are you going __________ (get) up tomorrow?
g What's the next thing that you're going __________ (eat)?
h When are you next __________ (see) your best friend?

Write true answers to the questions.

4 Put the verbs in parentheses into the correct form. Use the present progressive, *going to*, or *will/'ll* + infinitive. Sometimes more than one verb form is possible.

A: Why are you looking so happy?
B: I just got my tickets. I (1) 'm going (go) to New Orleans this weekend.
A: What? Just for the weekend?
B: Yes, it's Mardi Gras. I (2) __________ (leave) early on Saturday at 6:30 a.m.
A: Where (3) __________ (you spend) the night?
B: I don't know. I haven't thought about it. I guess I (4) __________ (look) for a hotel when I get there.
A: I have an idea. I (5) __________ (give) you Patricia's number. She has room in her apartment.
B: I think she (6) __________ (go) away this weekend. She usually does during Mardi Gras.
A: OK, well, I (7) __________ (ask) my parents. Maybe they know someone with a room. Anyway, what is Mardi Gras?
B: It's a big carnival. I (8) __________ (take) my camera, so I can show you the pictures when I get back.

016 **Listen and check.**

5 Underline the correct alternative.

a **Anybody / Everybody / Somebody** knows they're getting married – it's in all the newspapers.

b He talks so fast that **everyone / no one / someone** can understand what he's saying.

c He's so quiet. He never says **anything / everything / something**.

d I think that they live **anywhere / everywhere / somewhere** near here.

e She's unhappy about **anything / everything / something**. But I don't know what it is.

f There is **anybody / everybody / somebody** I'd like you to meet. I think you'll like him.

g There's **anything / nothing / something** worse than an office party. I hate them.

h We don't go **anywhere / everywhere / somewhere** on vacation; we just stay at home.

6 Complete the text with a word beginning with *every-*, *some-*, *any-*, or *no-*.

The party was terrible. (1) __Everything__ about it was terrible. It was (2) ______ out of town, and it took me ages to find it. When I arrived, there wasn't (3) ______ to eat and there was (4) ______ to drink that I liked. (5) ______ enjoyed it and (6) ______ went home early. For me, the worst thing was that I lost my cell phone. I looked (7) ______ for it, but with no luck. (8) ______ said that there were thieves at the party, so maybe they stole it.

VOCABULARY

1 Look at the wordsnake. Write down six things you find at festivals.

a ______ d ______
b ______ e ______
c ______ f ______

2 Complete the sentences with the words in Exercise 1.

Festima always begins with a (1) ______ through the town. Men wear animal (2) ______ over their faces and amazing (3) ______ made of leaves. They travel from all over West Africa to take part. Why? To dance! (4) ______ play energetic drum music and the (5) ______ party all night long. When they get hungry they don't need to go far. People selling (6) ______ set up all over the town.

3 Complete the sentences with the words in the box.

down	forward	in	of
~~off~~	on	over	up

a A firework went __off__ with an incredibly loud noise.

b I know you're sad now, but you'll get ______ it soon.

c I'm feeling tired and I think I'll stay ______ this evening.

d Look at this mess! Who's going to clean it ______?

e She's taking care ______ her baby brother tonight.

f The neighbors asked us to turn ______ the music, because they couldn't sleep.

g We're really looking ______ to seeing you.

h You should put ______ some warm clothes.

4 Complete the sentences with the words in the box.

clear	~~comment~~	decorating	
housework	mistake	research	wish

a She made an unfriendly *comment* about my hair.

b I've never made a ____________ that came true.

c I only made one ____________ on the test.

d Can I make it ____________ that this is very important?

e When we have done more ____________ we'll know the answer.

f We bought an old house and we need to do a lot of ____________.

g They pay someone to do the ____________ once a week.

5 Complete the questions with *do* or *make*.

a Are you going to *do* any exercise today?

b Do you ____________ a lot of noise when you get up in the morning?

c Do you ____________ much money?

d Do you always ____________ sure that you have everything you need before you leave home?

e How much homework did you ____________ yesterday?

f How much progress do you need to ____________ with your English this year?

g How often do you ____________ the ironing?

h Do you like to ____________ the dishes?

Write true answers to the questions.

6 Underline the correct alternative.

a Andrew decided to throw a **farewell / leaving / surprise** party for his girlfriend's birthday.

b He sent **hosts / invitations / welcomes** to all her friends.

c He told his guests he was having a **costume / eating / grill** party.

d He put up **balloons / dustpans / candles** and party lights.

e He wanted to create a romantic **atmosphere / ice-breaker / theme** with soft lighting.

f When his girlfriend arrived, everyone **mingled / delegated / greeted** her with a song.

7 Complete the conversations with the phrases in the box.

~~Are you doing anything~~	I'd really love to, but
I was wondering	That sounds great
What a shame	What do you think about
Where do you want to go?	Would you like to

a **Mike**: (1) *Are you doing anything* on Saturday?
Edith: No, I'm not. Why?
Mike: (2) ____________ if you'd like to come to the opera.
Edith: (3) ____________. What's playing?

b **Mike**: (4) ____________ going out for dinner tonight?
Pearl: Yes, good idea. I'd love to.
Mike: Great. (5) ____________.
Pearl: I'd like to try the new Italian restaurant. I've heard it's really good.

c **Mike**: (6) ____________ go to a music festival next weekend?
Ellie: (7) ____________ I'm afraid I'm busy next weekend. I have to go and see my grandmother.
Mike: (8) ____________. It sounds really good.
Ellie: Yes, I know, but I'm sorry. It's her eightieth birthday.

▶ 017 Listen and check.

PRONUNCIATION

1 Look at the underlined consonant sounds. Circle the word which has a different sound from the other words.

a	course	fancy	promise	special
b	as	is	this	was
c	brush	goes	has	music
d	ice	mess	noise	sound
e	shoe	shower	sure	worse
f	push	reason	shame	sugar

▶ 018 Listen and check.

2 Choose 12 words from Exercise 1 and write them in the correct column.

/s/	/z/	/ʃ/
course	*is*	*brush*

3 Underline the /s/, /z/, and /ʃ/ sounds in these words. Use a different color for each sound.

dresses	exercise	shirts	shoes
showers	shush!	surprise	

▶ 019 Listen and check.

LISTENING

1 Look at the pictures below. Which country do you think they show?

Brazil	the USA	Italy	Spain

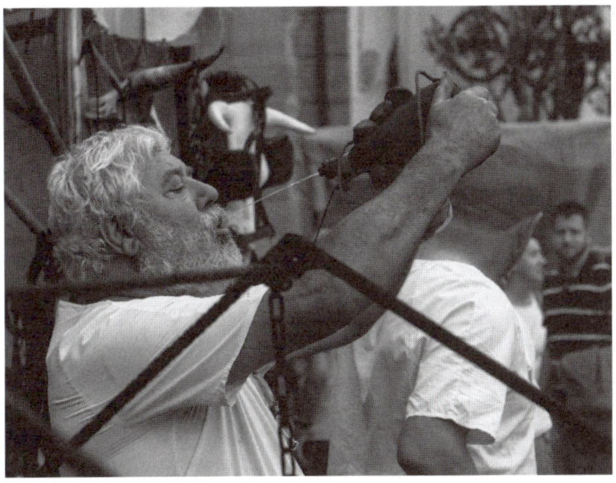

drinking from a bota

bull-running

2 020 **Cover the listening script. Listen to a description of a festival and number the events in the order in which they took place.**

Everybody throws wine over everybody else. ______
People go to a church service. ______
People run away from young bulls in the bullring. ______
The mayor leads a procession out of the town. ______
The procession returns to the town. ______
There is music and dancing in the town square. __1__
They have breakfast. ______

3 **Which two events in Exercise 2 did the speaker not take part in?**

4 **Find and <u>underline</u> the words in the script that tell us that:**

a the weather was good
b the speaker got up early
c the speaker walked a long way
d the speaker enjoyed the battle
e the speaker was wet with wine
f the speaker wanted to stay longer

The festival that I've enjoyed most takes place in a small town called Haro. Haro is in La Rioja, a wine region of Spain, and every June they have a festival called the Battle of Wine.

I arrived there on a beautiful sunny summer evening. There was a concert and dancing and so on in the town square. Some people stayed up celebrating all night, but I went to bed earlyish because the real fun began the next day.

I was dressed and ready before five-thirty. Everyone wore white T-shirts and a red scarf around their necks. In the center of the town, a man, the mayor, I think, was riding a horse and we all followed him on foot to a small mountain six or seven kilometers away.

On the mountainside there was a small church, and there was a service in the church, but I didn't go inside because there wasn't room for everybody. Anyway, it was better to be outside because after the church service, the battle began. Everyone had red wine. Some people had it in *botas* – containers made of animal skin – some had plastic bottles, some had filled balloons with wine, someone even had a huge thirty-liter container on his back. And you just throw it over anyone who is near you – especially if someone's T-shirt is still white! All the time, there were brass bands playing music and people were dancing, running around, throwing wine everywhere. Awesome! It all lasted about two hours before we had breakfast – snails cooked on a barbecue and a kind of champagne to drink.

After that, there was a procession back to the town, with everyone's T-shirts now pink. In the afternoon, everyone goes to the bullring, where they have young bulls that are running around – free – and you have to run away from them, but unfortunately I couldn't stay for that. I had to go to work, but even after a shower I could still smell the wine!

5 Edible

GRAMMAR

1 Decide if the nouns should be singular or plural and underline the correct alternative.

Customer: I'd like some grilled (1) **sardine / sardines**, and my husband will have your (2) **tuna / tunas** with (3) **garlic / garlics**.

Waiter: I'm afraid we don't have any (4) **fish / fishes** left, ma'am.

Customer: OK. Do you have any (5) **mussel / mussels**?

Waiter: I'm afraid we're completely out of (6) **seafood / seafoods**.

Customer: Hmm, well, we'll both have the (7) **veal / veals**. With roast (8) **vegetable / vegetables**.

Waiter: I'm afraid we don't have any (9) **meat / meats** left.

Customer: Oh, no. Maybe we'll just have two bottles of (10) **water / waters**. Could you bring some (11) **olive / olives** at the same time?

Waiter: Sure. We could make you some (12) **sandwich / sandwiches**, if you like.

Customer: No, thanks. But could you bring us some clean (13) **glass / glasses**? This one smells like old (14) **cod / cods**.

021 Listen and check.

2 Underline the correct alternative.

a I have a **little bit of** / **several** pens in my bag.
b I didn't have **enough** / **many** sleep yesterday.
c I speak **a little** / **none** French.
d I have **few** / **plenty of** free time later today.
e I don't eat **few** / **much** rice.
f I don't have **a lot of** / **several** power in my job.
g I know **little** / **a lot of** different teas.
h I go to the beach **a few** / **plenty** times every year.

Change the sentences to make them true for you.

3 Complete the sentences with the words in the box.

few	lot	many	
~~much~~	none	not	plenty

a Americans spend so ___much___ money on food.
b I need some milk, but there's ______ in the refrigerator.
c There are ______ many vegetables that I don't like.
d There is ______ of time to do the cooking.
e Very ______ people eat lobster because it's so expensive.
f We should all eat a ______ of fruit.
g I don't eat ______ cookies.

4 Rewrite these sentences using *used to*. Two of the sentences cannot be rewritten with *used to*. Leave them as they are.

a I hated my food when I was little.
I used to hate my food when I was little.
b I refused to eat everything.
______
c I didn't like meat, fish, or vegetables.
______
d My parents were worried about me.
______
e One day, they took me to the doctor.
______
f He told me to grow up.
______
g After that, I was even more difficult.
______

5 **Write the words in the correct order to complete the questions.**

When you were ten years old ...

a did have lunch to use you ?
... where did you use to have lunch?

b did drink in morning the to use you ?
... what ______________________

c be did favorite food to use your ?
... what ______________________

d go out restaurants to use you to ?
... did ______________________

e eat much to too use you ?
... did ______________________

f candy bars did prefer to use you ?
... what ______________________

Write true answers to the questions.

6 **Replace *used to* with *would* where it is possible.**

I *used to* have a job in a restaurant. Every morning, I *used to* go there at ten o'clock and I *used to* have coffee with all the others before work. The boss *used to* be very tough, but all of us liked him. At the end of a good day, he *used to* buy everyone a drink. On really good days, I *used to* make about $60 in tips. I *used to* be the best waitress there.

VOCABULARY

1 **Match the words on the left with those on the right.**

a	a bar of	matches
b	a bowl of	honey
c	a box of	gum
d	a bunch of	soap
e	a jar of	soup
f	a pack of	keys

2 **Complete the sentences with words from the left-hand column of Exercise 1. Sometimes more than one answer is possible.**

a He threw his pack of biscuits in the trash can.

b How much does this ______________ of bananas cost, please?

c I need to buy a large-size ______________ of tissues.

d I once ate a 250g ______________ of chocolate in one day.

e I'd like a ______________ of strawberry jelly, please.

f She often has a ______________ of cereal and milk for breakfast.

3 **Put the words in the box into the correct column.**

~~beans~~ cauliflower celery eggplant figs
garlic grapefruit leeks lettuce lime
lobster peach plum raspberries sausages
shrimp tuna turkey veal

Meat and fish	Vegetables	Fruit
	beans	

4 **Find and underline three strange dishes in the menu below. What would you choose for each course?**

MENU

Appetizers

Tomato and cucumber salad
Smoked salmon and cockroaches
Roasted red peppers and zucchini
Indian mussel curry

Entrées

Cabbage and bacon pie
Pasta bake with mushrooms and olives
Atlantic cod, fried potatoes, and spinach
Bitter radishes and crunchy grasshoppers
Spicy tuna and rice

Desserts

Fruit salad (melon, oranges, and mango)
Caterpillar and whiskey yogurt
Ice cream (cherry, chocolate, and coffee)
Strawberries and cream

5 Complete the sentences with the words in the box.

water	cheese	coffee	
egg	meal	shrimps	~~chocolate~~

a Which has more sugar – bitter or sweet __chocolate__?

b Which wakes you up more in the morning – strong or weak ______?

c Which is better for your health – a heavy or a light ______?

d Which might make you sick – a cooked or a raw ______?

e Which is more expensive – tap or bottled ______?

f Which smells more – strong or mild ______?

g Which taste better – fresh or frozen ______?

Write true answers to the questions.

6 Write the missing letters to complete the text.

~~a~~ a a b c e f g h h h

i l ~~n~~ n r s s t u y y

It was the worst meal I've ever had. The soup was from a (1) c a n and very (2) bl _ _ d. For the main course, the meat was (3) to _ _ _, (4) c _ ew _, and over-cooked, and I think they probably (5) bo _ _ ed the vegetables for over an hour. The French fries were (6) gr _ _ _ y and too salty. The bread was extremely dry and obviously not very (7) _ re _ _. For dessert, I had a (8) spi _ _ crème caramel–I found a piece of chilli pepper in it! Finally, they gave me a (9) _ it _ e _ cup of coffee, which was too disgusting to drink.

022 Listen and check.

7 Complete the conversation with the phrases in the box.

Both well done, please.
Excuse me, we're ready to order now.
Not quite. Could you give us a minute or two, please?
We'll both have the steak, please.
Yes, two glasses of water, please.
~~Yes, a table for two in the name of Smith.~~

Waiter: Good evening. Do you have a reservation?
Customer: (1) Yes, a table for two in the name of Smith.
Waiter: Thank you, sir. Please follow me.
Waiter: Are you ready to order yet?
Customer: (2) ______
Waiter: Sure. Would you like to order some drinks while you're deciding?
Customer: (3) ______
Customer: (4): ______
Waiter: Certainly. What can I get you?
Customer: (5) ______
Waiter: Very good. How would you like that done?
Customer: (6) ______

023 Listen and check.

PRONUNCIATION

1 024 Look at the following groups of words. Listen to the recording and notice how the middle word is pronounced with the sound /ə/. Practice saying the phrases.

a cup		milk
a pair	of	jeans
a kind		fish
something		drink
ready	to	go
things		do
problems		work
stay	at	home
dinner		eight
gin		tonic
steak	and	fries
rock		roll

2 Complete the mini-conversations with words from the middle column of Exercise 1.

a **Waiter:** What can I get you, sir?
Customer: Two glasses (1) __of__ water (2) ______ an order (3) ______ fries, please.

b **Elly:** Let's meet (4) ______ seven (5) ______ the station.
Anya: Yes, (6) ______ then we can go (7) ______ the theater.

025 Listen and check. Then practice the mini-conversations.

WRITING

Writing an email to make a complaint

1 Read the email. In which numbered blanks do these phrases (a–i) belong?

a as well as a full refund ____
b I am sure that you will understand ____
c I am writing this email to complain about ____
d I look forward to receiving ____
e I was dissatisfied with ____
f This was not what I expected ____
g To make matters worse ____
h was not of the highest standard ____
i You can imagine my disappointment when ____

FROM: twells@mail.com
TO: service@bellevuerestaurant.net
SUBJECT: Poor service and food!

Dear Sir / Madam,

... (1) ... the dinner that I ate in your restaurant last Saturday. ... (2) ... both the service and the quality of the food that was served.

Your restaurant was recommended to me by my brother, who assured me that you specialized in seafood of the highest quality. ... (3) ... I learned that you had no seafood left by the time I arrived. That, after all, was my reason for coming. What is more, the food that I was served ... (4) ... .
... (5) ... , the waiters were rude and unfriendly. ... (6) ... from a restaurant of your reputation. ... (7) ... my reasons for writing this email. ... (8) ... an apology, ... (9) ... .
I am attaching a copy of the receipt.

Sincerely,

T. Wells

026 Listen and check.

2 Look at the advertisement and the notes that you made during your vacation. Write an email of complaint to the manager of Bellevue Motel.

Bellevue Motel
at Atlantic City

Call us now to make a reservation.
609-522-0663

Limited places!

Beautiful ocean views

Family atmosphere

TV and shower in every room

Excellent restaurant

Special offers for July

We welcome children!

Notepad

Our room was at the back of the motel.
The TV didn't work.
The chef was on vacation!
When we went to pay, we were told we had to pay an extra summer supplement.
The children were terrified of a large dog that was always at the front desk.

6 Time

GRAMMAR

1 **<u>Underline</u> the correct alternative.**

a I sometimes get sick in **Monday morning / <u>January or February</u>**.

b I last went to a dance in **Friday / 2015**.

c I like listening to music in bed at **night / Friday night**.

d I always read the newspaper on **Sunday morning / the morning**.

e I like to get up late in **Sunday / the winter**.

f I often work on **night / the weekend**.

g My birthday is on **June 7 / June**.

h I was born at **five o'clock / the morning** in **five o'clock / the morning**.

Change the sentences to make them true for you.

2 **Complete the text with the best alternative: *at*, *on*, *in*, or *during*.**

I first met my wife (1) __in__ the spring of 2016, (2) ______ April 17 to be exact. It was (3) ______ a business trip to Miami, and (4) ______ Sunday morning, the 16th, I woke up with a terrible toothache. I needed to see a dentist, but that wasn't possible (5) ______ the weekend. (6) ______ night it was worse and I couldn't sleep. (7) ______ the morning, I managed to get an appointment for four o'clock that afternoon. (8) ______ my meetings that morning, my tooth was very painful and I was really glad to get to the dentist (9) ______ the afternoon. I made sure that I was (10) ______ time for the appointment! But as soon as the dentist walked in, she smiled at me and my pain went away. (11) ______ the evening, I took her out for dinner and (12) ______ July, we got married!

027 **Listen and check.**

3 **Complete these job descriptions with the words in the boxes.**

a

can	can't	~~don't have to~~	have to	should

I (1) __don't have to__ start work at any particular time. I (2) ____________ choose because I work for myself. I (3) ____________ work hard to make enough money, but in my job, you (4) ____________ work for more than eight hours a day. They say it's dangerous because people get tired, but I think they (5) ____________ change the law.

b

can	can't	don't have to	have to	should

We soccer players (1) ____________ work on the weekend, but we (2) ____________ work every day during the week. The boss is very strict and says we (3) ____________ go out the night before a game, but I very rarely play! I know I (4) ____________ fight for my place on the team, but my wife thinks I (5) ____________ find another team.

4 **Write a sentence using the word in italics, so that it means the same as the first sentence.**

a It's important for us to be in good physical condition. (*should*)
We ________________________________

b It's necessary to follow orders all the time. (*have*)
We ________________________________

c We're allowed to live with our family when we're not abroad. (*can*)
We ________________________________

d It isn't necessary to wear a uniform in the evenings. (*have*)
We ________________________________

VOCABULARY

1 **Look at the calendar and answer the questions. Today is July 19.**

July						
Sun	Mon	Tue	Wed	Thu	Fri	Sat
				1	2	3
4	5	6	7	8	9	10
11	12	13	14	15	16	17
18	19	20	21	22	23	24
25	26	27	28	29	30	31

a What were the dates of the weekend before last?
July 10 and 11. ______

b What is the date a week from tomorrow?
______

c What is the date five days from now?
______

d What is the date the Tuesday after next?
______

e What was the date the day before yesterday?
______

f What was the date two weeks ago?
______

g What was the date the Tuesday before last?
______

h What is the date a week from today?
______

2 **Match the definitions with the phrasal verbs in the box.**

calm down	come up with	cross off
get by	~~put off~~	rely on

a delay doing something that you do not want to do
put off ______

b draw a line through something on a list
______

c begin to feel more relaxed, or make someone do this
______

d have just enough of something so that you can do what you need to do
______

e think of something, such as an idea or a plan
______

f trust someone to do something for you
______

3 **Match the questions (a–f) with the responses (1–6).**

a Do you have to work *unsocial* hours?
b How long is your working day?
c How would you like your job to be different?
d Is your job very stressful?
e What kind of office do you work in?
f What kind of *qualifications* do you have?

1 I have a business diploma.
2 I usually do an eight-hour *shift*.
3 I'd like *flexible* hours so that I could come into work a little later some days.
4 It's *open-plan* with no dividing walls at all.
5 No, not at all. I do the usual nine to five.
6 Yes, very. We have to meet strict *deadlines* all the time.

a	b	c	d	e	f
5					

4 **Complete the text with the words in italics in Exercise 3.**

It's not a bad job and you don't need to have any (1) *qualifications*. I have to meet (2) ______, of course. I have to find ten new customers every day, and that means that I sometimes have to work a very long (3) ______ and very (4) ______ hours. But the boss is very (5) ______ about our hours if we do a good job. At least, it's better than my last job, where I worked in an (6) ______ office. I thought I was going to die in that job!

5 Complete the sentences with the words in the boxes.

1

confirm	attaching	~~Thank~~	writing

a ____Thank____ you for your telephone call earlier today.

b I am sorry to learn that you were not happy with the service provided by our company, and I am ______________ a complaint form.

c I would appreciate it if you could ______________ the details of your experience in ______________.

2

apply	position	response	résumé

a I am writing in ______________ to your advertisement in the *Sunday News*.

b As requested, I am attaching a ______________ and two letters of reference for your attention.

c I would like to ______________ for the ______________ of office assistant at your company.

3

appreciate	attend	available
hearing	received	

a Thank you for your email, which I ______________ yesterday.

b Unfortunately, I am not ______________ on the date you suggest in your email.

c I will, however, be free to ______________ an interview at any time during the following week.

d I would ______________ it if you could suggest a new date.

e I look forward to ______________ from you as soon as possible.

6 Write the missing letters.

a I hope that I get home i<u>n</u> time f_ _ the start of the game on TV.

b I've told you time and t_ _ _ a_ _ _ _, but you never listen.

c She had arrived way too early and she was looking for a way to _ _ _ l time.

d Some people say that we're _ _ _ _ing o_ _ of time to save the planet.

e They had a little time to s_ _ _ _, so they went for a walk around the town.

f Time really f_ _ _s when you're having fun, doesn't it?

g We have a lot of things to do, but we'll do them o_ _ _ _ a time.

h We're m_ _ing g_ _d time and we'll probably arrive early if we continue like this.

PRONUNCIATION

1 028 Listen to the recording and write the missing letters.

b	c	d	f	g	p	t	v

a _ a c k

b _ a c k

c _ o w n

d _ o w n

e l e a _ e

f l e a _

g _ l a s s

h _ l a s s

Listen again and practice saying the words.

2 029 Listen to the recording and cross out the words that you hear. Which is the first vertical column that you cross out?

1	2	3	4
add	at	back	bag
bush	cab	cap	cod
could	do	drew	dry
few	god	good	had
hat	of	off	push
ride	safe	save	too
true	try	view	write

3 030 Play the game again. Which vertical column do you cross out first this time?

1	2	3	4
add	at	back	bag
bush	cab	cap	cod
could	do	drew	dry
few	god	good	had
hat	of	off	push
ride	safe	save	too
true	try	view	write

LISTENING

1 031 **Cover the listening script and listen to an interview with Dr. Lee, an international expert on body clocks. Put the following actions at the best time on the body clock below.**

a avoid making important professional decisions
b have dinner
c drink alcohol
d go to sleep at night
e avoid people who are sick
f study
g play competitive sports like tennis

	1	2	3	4	5	6	7	8	9	10	11	12
A.M.			a									
	1	**2**	**3**	**4**	**5**	**6**	**7**	**8**	**9**	**10**	**11**	**12**
P.M.												

2 **Listen again and complete the sentences.**

a The hormones melatonin and cortisol affect how ___*tired*___ we feel.
b Many people have dinner when their sense of ______________ and ______________ is at its best.
c It's better to have an early dinner because the ______________ doesn't work well at night.
d It's a good idea to go to bed early because it's good for our ______________.
e The number of white blood cells in the body is ______________ at the start of the day.
f We can think fast after lunch, although the ______________ is slow.

Glossary
hormone
a substance that is produced by your body that helps it to develop and grow
liver
the part of your body that cleans the blood
white blood cells
the parts of your blood that defend the body against diseases

Presenter: I'd like to welcome Dr. Lee, an expert in chronobiology, who is with us in the studio this evening. Dr. Lee, I wonder if you could begin by telling us what chronobiology is exactly.

Dr. Lee: Yes, of course. Chronobiology is quite a young science. It studies how the bodies of animals are regulated by a kind of clock that tells them when it is best to do certain things – both physical things and mental things.

Presenter: Do you study humans, too?

Dr. Lee: Yes, of course. Humans are very sensitive to two hormones that are called melatonin and cortisol. These hormones affect how tired we feel. We have discovered, for example, that in the early hours of the morning, when most people are asleep, our body temperatures are at their lowest. This is the time when it's very easy to make mistakes, mistakes of judgment. So people like doctors, for example, who often have to work night shifts, need to be very careful.

Presenter: I imagine that the time we eat is very important?

Dr. Lee: Absolutely. Our sense of taste and smell is at its best between 6:00 and 8:00 p.m., so it's not surprising that many people have dinner at that time.

Presenter: Does that mean that I shouldn't eat later in the evening?

Dr. Lee: No, not necessarily. But the stomach doesn't work well at night, so it's best to eat earlier. However, the liver tends to work better after about 8:00 p.m., so that's the best time for alcoholic drinks. Different parts of the body work better at different times of the day. The skin, for example, grows most during the night between 11:00 p.m. and 1:00 a.m., so it's important that we don't go to bed too late.

Presenter: Are there any other important times we should know about?

Dr. Lee: Well, at the start of the day, the number of white blood cells you have is low, so that's not a good time to meet people with contagious diseases.

Presenter: Oh, I'll try to remember that!

Dr. Lee: The best time for *remembering* is early in the afternoon. This is when the body is slow, but the mind is quick. If you're learning a foreign language, for example, this is the time to do it, but leave your physical exercise until later, towards 4 or 5 o'clock. If you want to play a game of tennis, do it after you've learned your irregular verbs!

Presenter: OK! And when's the best time for interviews?

7 News

GRAMMAR

1 Underline the correct alternative.

a I don't mind <u>**being**</u> **/ to be** the center of attention.
b People tell **me / to me** that I'm perfect.
c I want **having / to have** a pierced nose.
d I can't stand **reading / to read** fashion magazines.
e I enjoy **spending / to spend** money.
f I need **getting / to get** a new camera.
g I never ask people **helping / to help** me.
h I've never tried **go / to go** on a diet.

Change the sentences to make them true for you.

2 Rewrite the sentences beginning with the words given.

a "Don't touch it," he told me.
He warned me not to touch it.
b "I'll be there at eight," she said.
She promised ______
c "Why don't you sue the photographers?" he asked me.
He suggested ______
d "The interest rate changes from time to time," she told me.
She explained ______
e "I'd better not leave this job," I thought.
I realized ______
f "Forget about me," he said to his wife.
He told ______
g "OK, I'll see you both later," she said.
She agreed ______
h "Could you stop being mean?" he asked her.
He asked ______

3 Complete the questions with the words in the box.

Are	be	been	being
Have	Is	~~was~~	were

a When __was__ your house built?
b Will your dinner ______ cooked for you this evening?
c ______ you ever described as "glamorous"?
d What was the last thing you ______ forced to do?
e ______ you ever been told to go away?
f ______ your private life talked about by other people?
g Are you ______ watched by anyone right now?
h Has your homework ______ checked recently?

Write true answers to the questions.

4 Complete the sentences with the verb in parentheses in the passive form. Use the simple present, simple past, or present perfect.

a The rock star Sonia Thorne __was arrested__ at Los Angeles airport last night. (arrest)
b She ______ after arriving on a flight from Miami. (stop)
c Almost two kilos of cocaine ______ in her bags. (find)
d This is the third time that Ms. Thorne ______ on drug charges. (arrest)
e However, she ______. (never / convict)
f Ms. Thorne ______ in a police station last night. (keep)
g Because of her arrest, her concert at the Hollywood Bowl ______. (cancel)
h It ______ that she will appear in court later today. (believe)

5 **Rewrite the following sentences using a passive verb.**

a The paparazzi followed the car for ten kilometers.
The car _was followed by the paparazzi for ten kilometers._

b People photograph her when she walks down the street.
She ______

c The newspaper will pay her $50,000 for the pictures.
She ______

d They are going to put the pictures on the front page of the newspaper.
The pictures ______

e Thieves stole an enormous sum of money from a Hollywood celebrity last night.
Last night, an enormous sum of money ______

f Police officers have accused the football player Ed Flower of burglary.
The football player, Ed Flower, ______

6 **Correct the following news stories by changing one verb in each story. Some need to be changed from active to passive, and some from passive to active.**

a

Donovan Thomas ~~was escaped~~ from prison in Rhode Island, in the USA, after serving 89 days of a 90-day sentence. He was caught and sentenced to an extra six months.

escaped

b

Philip Johnson, 32, from Prestonburg, Kentucky, shot himself in the chest because he wanted to see if it hurt. He was discovered that it hurts a lot.

______

c

Circus girl, Jasmine Brown, 22, jailed for six days by a court in San Diego. She was riding an elephant on a busy highway and she was not wearing any clothes.

______

d

André Gurmon, from Montreal, Canada, was put an advertisement in the newspaper. It said: "Ladies—write to me if you are bored with the man in your life." He received a reply from his wife.

______

e

Harrison Ford has several false teeth. Ford told the truth about his teeth after he voted sexiest man alive in a popular magazine.

______

f

Hollywood star, Tom Duffy, has been seen with his new girlfriend, the glamorous Dolores Barker. The happy couple was being visited Trinidad for a short vacation.

______

VOCABULARY

1 **Match the definitions with the words in the box.**

desperate	hypocritical	insensitive
obsessed	~~photogenic~~	unflattering

a a person who looks good in pictures
photogenic

b believing something is so important that you think about it all the time
______

c making someone seem less pleasant or attractive than usual
______

d needing or wanting something very much
______

e not noticing or caring about the feelings or needs of other people
______

f saying that you believe certain things but behaving in a different way
______

2 **Complete the sentences with words from Exercise 1.**

a He was extremely _insensitive_ and didn't listen to me at all.

b I'm ______ to see her again.

c I'm the least ______ person in the world and I don't have a single good picture of myself.

d Money, money, money, that's all she thinks about. She's completely ______.

e Stop being so ______. I know you don't really believe what you're saying.

f It's an interesting painting of her, but it's a little ______.

3 Match the TV shows with the descriptions.

Tonight's top shows

Fugitives! (Channel 7, 7:00 p.m.-8.00 p.m.)
Parking Ticket (The Laugh Channel, 9:30 p.m.-10:15 p.m.)
Family Court (BBTV, 8:00 p.m.-9:00 p.m.)
Stop, Thief (TV22, 7:45 p.m.-8:30 p.m.)
Paparazzi Chase (Filmplus, 8:45 p.m.-10:30 p.m.)
Hot Gossip (BBTV, 11:00 p.m.-11:55 p.m.)

a Celebrities in the news – find out which Hollywood star is suspected of leading a double life.
Hot Gossip

b Comedy show about a glamorous officer in the highway patrol.
____

c Documentary about six convicted criminals who escaped from a high-security jail.
____

d Enjoyable action movie about a photographer who has to hide from a mysterious man in black.
____

e Ordinary members of the public in the fight against crime. This week: a burglar is caught in an embarrassing situation.
____

f Proceedings are dramatically stopped in Kate's divorce when the judge has a heart attack.
____

4 Complete the sentences with the verbs in the box.

~~arrested~~	committed	escaped
kidnapped	stolen	

a The police *arrested* her after a long car chase.
b She had ________ the car that she was driving.
c She had ________ more than fifty different crimes in twenty-four hours.
d In her worst crime, she had ________ a ten-year-old child.
e She ________ after only two weeks by climbing over a wall.

5 Complete the email with the words in the box.

Actually	Anyway	~~great~~	Guess	let
Love	news	Talking	thing	touch

Dear Pia,
It was (1) *great* to hear from you. I didn't know the (2) ________ about Anna and Giorgio, but I'm not sorry to hear it. They weren't getting along at all.
(3) ________, I never liked Giorgio, and Anna deserves someone better than him. The good (4) ________ now is that she can look for someone else.
I heard from Sue, who was in (5) ________ last week. She's looking forward to her baby and she's had all the tests. Apparently, it's a boy, so her husband is happy, but I think she wanted a girl.
(6) ________ of happy couples, it sounds as though you're very happy with your new boss!
(7) ________, I was so happy to hear that you're taking a vacation in August. (8) ________ what? I'm on vacation then, too. I'll (9) ________ you know my exact dates when I have them. Why don't we do something together?
(10) ________,
Ian

6 Number the lines in the correct order to make a mini-conversation.

Conversation 1
a ☐ I was arrested last night.
b ☐ Oh, no. I'm sorry to hear that. What happened?
c ☐ That's terrible. Who did they think you were?
d ☐ The police thought I was someone else.
e ☐ You don't look too happy. How are things going?

Conversation 2
a ☐ Mine, actually.
b ☐ Yes, I'm going to an engagement party.
c ☐ Are you doing anything interesting this weekend?
d ☐ Lucky you! Whose is it?

Conversation 3
a ☐ Guess what?
b ☐ How annoying!
c ☐ I got a parking ticket this afternoon.
d ☐ What?

032 **Listen and check.**

PRONUNCIATION

1 033 **Listen and repeat the sentences. Notice the way that some words are joined together.**
a Kate Moss asked‿us‿not‿to take pictures‿of‿her daughter.
b People also want‿to‿think that they're just‿normal people.
c She stopped‿to ask‿her‿if she was‿OK.
d They want to know what he's going‿to do‿about‿it.

2 034 **Listen and figure out the correct spelling of the following phrases.**
a wannathink
want to think
b promistachange
____
c forgeddaboudit
____

d jusdoingajob

______

e wotchagonnadoaboudit

______

f wazityafirstime

______

WRITING

Writing an essay

Linking sentences with *although*, *despite*, *however*

1 **Read the examples in the box, showing how to contrast ideas using *although*, *despite*, and *however*.**

Contrasting ideas

although
Although I'm a fan of Alicia Keys, I'm not interested in her private life.
He claims his marriage is happy, although he was seen at a New York club with his personal assistant.

despite
Despite the fact that I'm a fan of Alicia Keys, I'm not interested in her private life.
He claims his marriage is happy, despite the fact that he was seen in a New York club with his personal assistant.

however
I'm a fan of Alicia Keys. However, I'm not interested in her private life.
He claims his marriage is happy. However, he was seen at a New York club with his personal assistant.

2 **Complete the sentences with *although*, *despite*, or *however*.**

a A lot of people buy gossip magazines, ___despite___ the fact that they contain a lot of trash.

b Young people often look up to movie and rock stars. ______, these celebrities are not always good role models.

c ______ some celebrities say they hate the tabloid press, they sometimes sell their stories to these newspapers for a lot of money.

d ______ I like some movie stars, I'm not interested in reading about their love lives.

e Most people like to read gossip, ______ the fact that they claim the opposite.

f Newspapers should not be allowed to print lies. ______, it's important for the press to remain free.

3 **Complete the sentences with the words in the box.**

believe	conclusion	considered	more
~~opinion~~	point	remember	wrong

a In my ___opinion___, it is wrong for the press to photograph the private lives of movie stars.

b Personally, I ______ that we have the right to know about their lives.

c However, it is important to ______ that the press sometimes goes too far.

d Although some people feel that it is ______ to print these stories, many stars do not mind at all.

e However, perhaps the most important ______ is what the individual celebrities think about it.

f What is ______, some celebrities will sell their stories to the press.

g All things ______, I do not think that we should ban this kind of reporting.

h In ______, I would say that we should ban the reporting of these scandals.

4 **Write an essay, using the title and essay plan below.**

a First, make a plan on a piece of paper. Use some of the ideas from Exercise 2 to help you.

b Before you start, look at the language in Exercise 3 to help you.

Celebrity scandals* in the press: should they be banned?

Paragraph 1: Introduction
Explain that some people think that the reporting of celebrity scandals in the press should be banned. You might want to give an example of such a scandal.

Paragraph 2: Give your opinion and choose at least two reasons for this. Also give arguments against your reasons.

Paragraph 3: State the opposite opinion with at least two reasons that could be given for it. Argue against these reasons.

Paragraph 4: Conclusion
Give your opinion again.

*scandals = reports in the press about shocking behavior

8 Travel

GRAMMAR

1 **Can you name the countries: A, B, and C? Choose from this list:**

Angola
Brazil
Colombia
Cuba
Honduras
Mozambique
Uruguay
Venezuela

Country	A	B	C
Population	about 32 million	about 208 million	about 11 million
Official language	Spanish	Portuguese	Spanish
Climate	tropical	tropical and sub-tropical	semi-tropical
Main exports	oil, aluminum	iron, steel, soybean, machinery, coffee	sugar, tobacco, coffee
Highest mountain	4,979 m	2,993 m	1,974 m

2 **Look at the table above again and complete the sentences with the words in the box.**

Country A

~~couldn't~~	definitely	guess	might

a It *couldn't* be Brazil, because they speak Portuguese in Brazil.
b I think it ___________ be Colombia, because there are some high mountains there, aren't there?
c I ___________ it could be Venezuela. I think they have lots of oil.
d It ___________ isn't Uruguay, because I'm sure that it isn't tropical.

Country B

couldn't	certainly	could	must

a It's ___________ not Cuba, because that's Spanish-speaking.
b And it ___________ be Honduras – that's not a very industrialized country.
c It ___________ be Angola – I think they have a climate like that.
d It ___________ be Brazil. None of the other countries have so many people.

Now write similar sentences about Country C.

a ___________
b ___________
c ___________
d ___________

3 **Read the text and number the sentences below in the order in which they happened in Michael Crichton's life.**

Michael Crichton, the author of *Jurassic Park*, was one of the world's greatest travelers. In his autobiography, *Travels*, he describes how he began "serious" traveling when he was 30 and he went to Bangkok. He then began his amazing adventures, which included diving with sharks off Tahiti, watching gorillas in the Congo, and living in the jungle in New Guinea.

It all began in Los Angeles, where Crichton was writing movies for Hollywood. He had given up his studies at Harvard Medical School and he had separated from his wife, because he wanted to spend his time writing. At Harvard, he had already sold one movie, *The Andromeda Strain*, to Hollywood, and he had begun to lose interest in medicine.

In LA, he made the successful science-fiction movie *Westworld*, but he then fell into a depression and did not know what to do next. He decided to go to Bangkok, because a friend of his who lived there had invited him. It was the beginning of an incredible life of traveling.

a A friend invited him to Bangkok. ___
b He fell into a depression. ___
c He left Harvard. ___
d He made *Westworld*. ___
e He sold *The Andromeda Strain* to Hollywood. 1
f He went to Bangkok. ___
g He went to Los Angeles. ___
h He went to Tahiti and the Congo. ___

4 **Put the verbs in parentheses into the simple past or the past perfect.**

a Before he left Harvard, Michael Crichton *had already sold* (already / sell) a movie to Hollywood.
b He wanted to leave Harvard because he ___________ (think) the classes were boring.

c He separated from his wife before he __________ (go) to LA.

d He went to Los Angeles because he __________ (decide) to spend his time writing.

e After he went to Los Angeles, he __________ (fall) into a depression.

f He remembered that a friend __________ (invite) him to Thailand.

g When he arrived in Bangkok, his friend __________ (meet) him at the airport.

h Before he went to Bangkok, he __________ (never / be) outside America or Europe.

5 **Write three true sentences about the topics below.**

- three things that you had done before ten o'clock this morning
- three things you had eaten or drunk before lunchtime yesterday
- three people you had spoken to today before you began this exercise

VOCABULARY

1 **Complete the sentences with the words in the box.**

between	far	~~in~~	in	not
of	of	on	on	to

a I live (1) __in__ the north-west (2) __________ my country not (3) __________ from the mountains. My village is (4) __________ the north of Chiang Mai, which is the nearest big city.

b I live in the south-west of the country. The town is (5) __________ the coast, but we're (6) __________ far from the mountains.

c I live (7) __________ the north of the country. The town is (8) __________ a lake to the north of Milan.

d I live on an island in Lake Titicaca (9) __________ the mountains (10) __________ Peru and Bolivia.

Which place (a, b, c, or d) is shown in the picture?

2 **Complete the sentences with the words in the box.**

ancient	~~Buddhist~~	high-rise
skyline	snow-capped	waterfall

a There are seven temples at the __Buddhist__ monastery of Taktshang, Bhutan, which hangs from a cliff at 700 meters above the river below.

b There are many good ski resorts in the __________ Rocky Mountains.

c The __________ ruins of Stonehenge were possibly a temple to a sun god.

d Water from the Tortum Lake, 100 kilometers north of Erzurum in eastern Turkey, falls 48 meters in a spectacular __________ into the river below.

e You can get a good view of the Manhattan __________ from the Statue of Liberty.

f You can go to the roof of many of the __________ buildings in Manhattan.

3 **Underline the correct alternative below to complete the texts.**

The Yucatán Peninsula

Most of the beaches are (1) by apartment buildings and restaurants. They are especially (2) with tourists and the beautiful sands are full of (3). But there are still some (4) places. The prettiest part of the coast is Puerto Morelos, where you get spectacular (5) of the ocean.

The Sussex Coast

The towering white (6) of Sussex in the (7) part of England begin at the headland of Beachy Head. You can follow the coastal path all the way to Brighton. In Brighton, there are some great stores and cute little pubs on (8) streets. The Grand Hotel, (9) the beach, is a great place for afternoon tea.

1 **packed / popular / surrounded**
2 **hidden / overlooking / popular**
3 **beach communities / lounge chairs / white sands**
4 **local / sandy / unspoiled**
5 **coves / lagoons / views**
6 **bay / beaches / cliffs**
7 **island / southern / watersports**
8 **coral / hidden / overlooking**
9 **dynamite / overlooking / ranging**

4 Complete the sentences with the words in the box.

all or nothing	come and go	give or take
neat and tidy	~~peace and quiet~~	sooner or later
	take it or leave it	

a I like to work very early in the morning, when I can have some _peace and quiet_.
b I don't mind tea, but I can ____________.
c I always keep my desk ____________.
d My English class lasts an hour, ____________ a few minutes.
e When I meet someone new, I either like them or I can't stand them – it's ____________.
f During our English classes, we can ____________ as we please.
g I have exams at the end of the year and ____________ I'll need to start some serious studying.

Check (✓) the sentences that are true for you.

5 Match the directions (a, b, and c) from City Hall (*A*) to three different subway stations (1, 2, 3 or 4).

a Go out of City Hall and take a right. Go to the end of the street, take a right again, and then take the third street on your left. You'll see a subway station at the end of the street.
Subway station ______
b Go out of City Hall and take a right. At the end of the street, take a left and then take the first street on your right. Go straight until you get to the end. Take a right and you'll see a subway station on the other side of the street.
Subway station ______
c Go out of City Hall and take a left. Follow the street to the end and then take a right. After that, I think it's the first street on the right again, and you go on until you see the subway station in front of you.
Subway station ______

6 Write directions from City Hall (A) to a restaurant (B).
a ____________
b ____________
c ____________
d ____________
e ____________
f ____________

PRONUNCIATION

1 Write the missing letters to complete the words. The words in each group have the same vowel sound.

a /ɔ/

a	al	~~au~~	aw

a u thor   f _ _ l   s _ _   w _ ter

b /ɜr/

er	ir	or	ur

p _ _ son   c _ _ ving   w _ _ st   f _ _ st

c /ɑr/

ar	ear

h _ _ _ t   g _ _ den   _ _ m   m _ _ ket

035 Listen and repeat.

2 Put the words in the box into three groups according to the vowel sound.

~~all~~	ball	~~birds~~	bought
~~car~~	girl	hardly	large
part	return	start	surf
wall	water	world	

/ɔ/	/ɜr/	/ɑr/
all	birds	car

036 Listen and check. Repeat the words.

LISTENING

1 037 Cover the listening script and listen to six people talking about their vacations. Decide if they enjoyed their vacation or not. Put ☺ or ☹ in the box.

1	2	3	4	5	6

2 Listen again and match a topic from the box to each of the speakers.

Topic	Speaker
entertainment	
food	
hotel	
trip	
money and prices	
weather	

3 Listen again. Are the statements true (T) or false (F)?

Speaker 1

a They didn't like the restaurants or excursions. ______

b They didn't have enough money. ______

Speaker 2

c The vacation was very tiring. ______

d They sometimes slept during the day. ______

Speaker 3

e The hotel was not very clean. ______

f The hotel staff was very friendly. ______

Speaker 4

g The plane was only a little late. ______

h They missed the train. ______

Speaker 5

i They didn't enjoy their first meal. ______

j The restaurants in the town were very good. ______

Speaker 6

k They were unhappy about the snow. ______

l The weather had been better the previous year. ______

1 The resort was great with a beautiful sandy beach. The problem was that everything cost a fortune. Fantastic restaurants, amazing excursions, windsurfing, diving, they had everything, but basically we did nothing at all because we couldn't afford it. After two days, we had spent all our money, so we just ate sandwiches after that, and watched everyone else enjoying themselves.

2 I was dead by the end of it. I've always wanted to go, so I decided to really enjoy myself. We didn't do much during the day because we needed our sleep, but in the evenings we saw a musical and then went dancing at a different place every night. Awesome! I can't wait to get back!

3 Yes, fantastic. The hotel was an ugly high-rise building – they hadn't even finished building it. It was absolutely filthy, and there didn't seem to be anyone working there. Oh yes, there was a man at reception, but he was asleep most of the time. It was the perfect destination for your worst enemy.

4 When we got to the check-in they said there was a short delay. Six hours later, we finally got on to an ancient plane, and when we were airborne, I just closed my eyes and hoped. When we arrived, we were too late for the train and, in any case, they had lost our baggage somewhere.

5 On the first day, we went down to the hotel restaurant and it was awful. They served us some kind of fish head in a spicy sauce. Ugh! So for the rest of the time we decided to go downtown where there were restaurants on every corner. We found some really amazing places and we couldn't wait for dinner time to arrive.

6 The funny thing is that although it was very cold, I actually got a little bit of sunburn. There had been a lot of snow just before we got there, so conditions were perfect. The resort was really at its best. It's a shame it wasn't like that last year.

9 Opinions

GRAMMAR

1 **Write true sentences for you using the verbs *tell* and *say*.**

____

____

____

____

____

____

____

____

____

____

2 **Put the movie quotes into reported speech and remember that the tenses move back. You will need to change some of the pronouns.**

a "Life is like a box of chocolates." (*Forrest Gump*)
His mother said that life was like a box of chocolates.

b "I'm coming for you." (*A Nightmare on Elm Street*)
Freddy told the children ____

c "You broke my heart, Fredo." (*The Godfather II*)
He told Fredo ____

d "His eyes have made love to me all evening." (*Camille*)
She said ____

e "I'll be back." (*The Terminator*)
He said ____

f "I'm going to make him an offer he can't refuse." (*The Godfather*)
He said ____

g "I had a farm in Africa." (*Out of Africa*)
She said ____

h "We'll always have Paris." (*Casablanca*)
Her told her ____

3 **Rewrite the text in direct speech.**
She told me that her favorite movie was *Titanic*. She explained that she had already seen it six times and that she was going to watch it again tonight. She said that she was a great fan of Kate Winslet and that she was hoping to meet her one day. She said that she particularly liked the ending, although it always made her cry. She said that she didn't find Leonardo DiCaprio very attractive, but she thought he was a great actor.

My favorite movie is Titanic. I ...

____

038 **Listen and check.**

4 **Correct the grammatical mistakes in four of the sentences below. Check (✓) the correct sentences.**

a She asked me who my favorite living author was.
✓

b She asked me what was the title of his last book.
____

c She asked me how many books he had written.
____

d She asked me which book had I read first.
____

e She asked me I was going to read any of his books again.
____

f She asked me whether I had read all his books.
____

g She asked me did I know anything about his life.
____

h She asked me what I was reading now.
____

Put the questions into direct speech.

a ____
b ____
c ____
d ____
e ____
f ____
g ____
h ____

5 Put the questions into reported speech, moving the tenses back.

a Did you enjoy it?
She asked me *if I had enjoyed it.*

b Who are the main characters?
She asked me ______________________

c How does the story begin?
She asked me ______________________

d Would you like to read it again?
She asked me ______________________

e What will you read next?
She asked me ______________________

f Did anyone recommend the book to you?
She asked me ______________________

g Was it easy to get into?
She asked me ______________________

h Do you ever stop reading a book before the end?
She asked me ______________________

VOCABULARY

1 Underline the correct alternative.

a The black and white **photography** / **premiere** was especially beautiful.

b The movie has a very happy **ending** / **hit**.

c It was a real **musical** / **tearjerker** and everybody was crying.

d I had to read the **fantasy** / **subtitles** because I couldn't understand what they were saying.

e The **plot** / **soundtrack** included two excellent songs by Elton John.

f The movie was **based on** / **set in** New York in the twenty-third century.

g I'm not sure whether it's a horror movie or a **storyline** / **thriller** – both, I guess.

2 Match the movie titles (a–h) with the types of movies (1–8).

a *The First Kiss*
b *Cut, Burn, Kill*
c *Al Capone and the Chicago Mafia*
d *My Girlfriend's Sense of Humor*
e *Mysterious Planet*
f *The Confident Cowboy*
g *They Died for their Country*
h *CIA: Secret Agent*

1 gangster movie
2 horror movie
3 love story
4 romantic comedy
5 science-fiction movie
6 spy movie
7 war movie
8 western

a	b	c	d	e	f	g	h
3							

3 Write the missing letters.

a My favorite (1) alb *u m* is called *Live at the Roxy* and my favorite song is the eighth (2) tra _ _, *No Woman, No Cry*. It's a recording of the great (3) regg _ _ singer, Bob Marley, performing (4) li _ _ at a (5) g _ _ in West Hollywood in 1976. I know the (6) lyr _ _ _ to all his songs and I love singing them. I play them at full volume on my (7) spea _ _ _ _ at home and annoy the neighbors.

b I can't stand modern music like (1) tec _ _ _ or (2) hip- _ _ _. I prefer (3) class _ _ _ _ music, like Beethoven or Mozart. I especially enjoy going to the (4) ope _ _. I play the violin in an (5) orche _ _ _ _ in my town and I also play in a folk (6) ba _ _. We do a lot of traditional (7) dan _ _ music.

4 Complete the text with the words in the box.

chapters	character	cover	ending	get
gripping	~~novel~~	paperback	plot	put

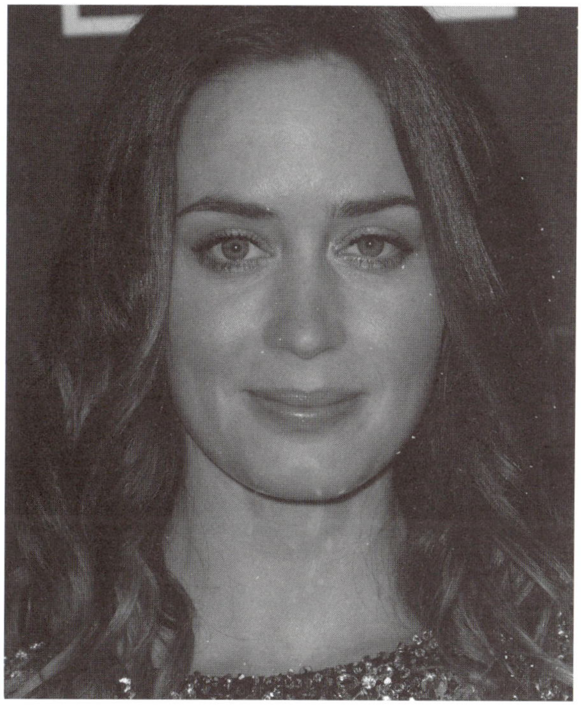

The last (1) *novel* I read was called *The Girl on the Train*. The reviews all said it was (2) ____________ and that you couldn't (3) ____________ it down after you'd started reading it. But after about four (4) ____________, I was still finding it hard to (5) ____________ into. The main (6) ____________ is Rachel Watson, a 32-year-old alcoholic who is obsessed with a couple she watches from the train every day. She often has blackouts and can't remember anything when she wakes up. The (7) ____________ gets complicated when one of the characters is murdered. The best part of the story is the (8) ____________, when the murderer is revealed. The (9) ____________ of the (10) ____________ edition of the book shows a picture from the movie that is based on the book. In the movie, Rachel Watson is played by actress Emily Blunt.

5 Complete the adjectives with *ing* or *ed*.

a He's so annoy*ing* – I really don't like him at all.
b I was so bor_____. I almost fell asleep.
c You may find this quite challeng_____, but tell me if you have a problem.
d She was a little confus_____ after his terrible explanation.
e He was very disappoint_____ with his performance when he learned that he hadn't won.
f It's one of the most excit_____ movies I've ever seen.
g Her autobiography was absolutely fascinat_____ and I couldn't put it down.
h I usually feel more relax_____ after a cup of hot chocolate.
i It's such an amazing story that I felt really inspir_____ after reading it.

6 Complete the conversations with the phrases (a–h).

a As far as I'm concerned
b do you know what I think
c do you think
d Don't you think
e I agree
f I'm not so sure
g see your point
h that's true, but

A: (1) ___*d*___ that's absolutely fantastic?
B: Definitely. (2) _______, he's the best artist in the world today.
A: Yes, (3) _______ with you. In fact, if you ask me, he's the best artist in the world ever!
B: Yes, probably. I think this is definitely his best painting.
A: Oh, (4) _______ about that. He's done so many great paintings.
C: What (5) _______ of that picture?
D: It's awful. In fact, (6) _______? A baby could paint better than that.
C: Yes, (7) _______ a baby might choose more attractive colors.
D: Yes, I (8) _______.

039 **Listen and check.**

PRONUNCIATION

1 040 **Listen and check (✓) the words that you hear.**

a	day	die ✓
b	fail	file
c	late	light
d	main	mine
e	tape	type
f	wait	white

2 **Put the words in the box in the correct column according to the vowel sound.**

~~age~~	~~buy~~	change	child	claim	cry
date	great	guy	mind	night	quite
save	strange	way	wild		

/eɪ/	/aɪ/
age	*buy*

041 **Listen and check. Repeat the words.**

WRITING

Writing a movie review
Making generalizations

1 **Read the movie review and check (✓) the topics that are mentioned.**

- the cast ✓
- the ending ☐
- the plot ☐
- the script ☐
- the soundtrack ☐
- the special effects ☐

Movie Review

Guardians of the Galaxy is a science-fiction superhero movie that was a big hit in 2014. It was co-written and directed by James Gunn. *Guardians of the Galaxy* is based on the characters in a series of Marvel comic books. It stars Chris Pratt, Zoe Saldana, Dave Bautista and Vin Diesel and there are many other well-known actors, too.

The movie tells the story of Peter Quill, who is kidnapped by space pirates as a child. 26 years later, Peter organizes a group of criminals to save the galaxy from the evil Ronan. Set in a fantasy universe, the plot is not always easy to understand, but on the whole the details of the story are not terribly important.

The script is very funny and the acting is generally excellent. Chris Pratt, who plays Peter Quill, brings plenty of energy to the many fight scenes in the movie. I was especially impressed by the soundtrack. It includes twelve songs from the 70s and 80s and even topped the US charts for a few weeks.

Guardians of the Galaxy is full of action and it's funny at the same time. As a piece of Hollywood entertainment, I thoroughly recommend it.

2 **Find phrases in the review that you can replace with the phrases below.**

a I particularly liked
b it is certainly worth seeing
c The movie is about
d Taking place in
e The starring roles are taken by
f the story is hard to follow
g very popular with movie-goers

3 **Look at the examples in the box. Then choose the best way to complete the sentences about a movie you know.**

Making generalizations	
On the whole, *In general,* *By and large,*	the acting is excellent
The acting is *generally* excellent.	

a On the whole, the plot is **a little confusing** / **not terribly believable** / **very engaging**.
b In general, the main characters of the movie are **a little disappointing** / **very convincing** / **very interesting**.
c By and large, the action scenes are **boring** / **thrilling** / **very well done**.
d The movie's soundtrack is generally **just right** / **quite inspiring** / **very annoying**.

4 **Write a review of a movie that you have seen. Use the paragraph plan below to help you.**

Paragraph 1
- What is the movie title?
- What kind of movie is it?
- When was it made?
- Who stars in it?
- Who directed it?
- How successful or popular was it?

Paragraph 2
- Where is it set?
- Who are the main characters?
- What happens in the movie? (Use the simple present to tell the story of the movie.)

Paragraph 3
- What did you like or dislike about the movie?
- What were the acting, the script, the soundtrack, etc. like?
- Were some parts of the movie better or worse than others?

Paragraph 4
- On the whole, did you enjoy the movie?
- Would you recommend it to other people?
- Why or why not?

10 Childhood

GRAMMAR

1 Delete the relative pronoun that is not possible.

a ... a sister **that** / ~~**which**~~ / **who** doesn't pull my hair!
b ... a house **that** / **which** / **who** has a big backyard.
c ... a school **that** / **which** / **who** I like.
d ... a teacher **that** / **which** / **who** doesn't give much homework.
e ... a friend **that** / **which** / **who** will let me win our games.
f ... a lot of cousins **that** / **which** / **who** are the same age as me.
g ... hair **that** / **which** / **who** is dark and curly.

2 Join the pairs of sentences with a relative clause.

a My dad is a nice guy. He gives me lots of presents.
My dad is a nice guy who gives me lots of presents.

b Dad lives with a new girlfriend. She doesn't like me.
____
____

c She has a daughter. I sometimes play with her.
____
____

d They have a house by the ocean. I really like it.
____
____

e My mom and I have a small apartment. She's really proud of it.
____
____

f Mom has a job. It's not very well paid.
____
____

g She works for a man. He looks like my father.
____
____

h This is a picture of my dad. I drew it.
____
____

3 Choose the most logical way to complete the sentences with *if* or *unless*.

a You'll never find a good job *unless* you go to college.
b Children are often unhappy __________ they have pushy parents.
c Children are much happier __________ they are brought up in the countryside.
d __________ you want your children to be successful, they have to learn English.
e You shouldn't have children __________ you have a lot of money.
f Life is very hard __________ you come from a rich family.
g Children never learn __________ you yell at them from time to time.

Check (✓) the sentences that you agree with.

4 Rewrite the sentences in Exercise 3 that contain *unless*. Replace *unless* with *if* and make any other necessary changes.

You'll never find a good job if you don't go to college.
____
____
____
____
____

5 **Correct the mistake in each sentence.**

a Do you know why ~~did Hayley run~~ *Hayley ran* away from home?

b Can you tell me this was the first time?

c Do you think if she's been sick recently?

d Could you tell me if does she have a boyfriend?

e Do you know where she did go?

f Do you think that she having problems at school?

g Do you have any idea will she do it again?

6 **Change the direct questions into indirect questions.**

a Do children have too much freedom?
Do you think *children have too much freedom?*

b Where is your son now?
Do you have any idea ______

c Is your child under stress at school?
Can you tell me ______

d What do your children think of you?
Could you tell me ______

e Are your children happy?
Do you know ______

f Is school more important than the family in a child's education?
Do you think ______

VOCABULARY

1 **Complete the phrasal verbs with a preposition.**

a I remember that my neighbors used to yell *at* me every time I kicked my ball into their backyard.

b I didn't mind helping with the cooking, but I hated cleaning ______.

c I was a very independent child and my parents knew that there was no need to worry ______ me.

d I wasn't a very good child and my parents were always telling me ______ for something or other.

e When I came home late, my parents sat ______ waiting for me.

f On Saturday evenings, a babysitter came to take care ______ me when my parents were out.

g When my parents came to tuck me ______, they always gave me a big kiss.

h My parents died when I was in my teens and I was brought ______ by my grandparents.

2 **Match the dictionary definitions with the phrasal verbs in Exercise 1.**

1 care for someone or something and make certain that they have everything they need; 2 be responsible for something

a *take care of*

1 [often passive] Take care of a child until he or she becomes an adult; 1a teach a child to behave in a particular way or to have particular beliefs; 1b used for saying where or how someone lived when they were a child

b ______

informal criticize someone for doing something wrong

c ______

feel nervous and upset because you keep thinking about a problem that you have or could have in the future

d ______

to go to bed later than usual

e ______

put a child into bed and make sure that they are warm and comfortable by covering them well

f ______

say something to someone in a loud voice, usually because you are angry

g ______

make a place look better by putting things in the correct place

h ______

3 **Put the words in order to complete the questions.**
When you were 13 years old, ...

a did do make parents the dishes you your ?
did your parents make you do the dishes?

b a did have let cell phone they you ?
____

c did dinner eat front in let of the they TV you ?
____

d did make they room clean up you your ?
____

e horror did movies let they you watch ?
____

f a at did friend's house let sleep they you?
____

Write true answers to the questions.

____

____

____

____

____

____

4 **Rewrite the sentences using *make* or *let*.**

a My parents forced me to go to church every Sunday.
My parents *made me go to church every Sunday.*

b The boss never allows us to take a day off.
The boss ____________________

c I don't allow the dog to come into the house.
I ____________________

d You're going to force me to get angry.
You're ____________________

e They didn't allow us to have any freedom.
They ____________________

f Will you allow me to come with you?
Will you ____________________

g Don't force her to talk if she doesn't want to.
Don't ____________________

5 **Complete the sentences with the words in the box.**

~~for~~	like	looks	
of	thing	use	with

Chopsticks fan

A: Have you seen this? It's a chopsticks fan.
B: A what? What's it (1) *for*?
A: It's a fan that you attach to your chopsticks and you (2) ________ it to cool down your food while you're eating.

Butter stick

A: Could you pass me the butter stick, please?
B: The butter stick? What does it look (3) ________?
A: It's that thing over there that (4) ________ like a lipstick or a tube of glue. It's for putting butter on your bread.

Banana holder

A: Excuse me. Do you sell banana holders?
B: Banana holders? I'm sorry, what do you do (5) ________ them?
A: You put a banana in them. It's the same shape as a banana. It's made (6) ________ plastic and it's a (7) ________ you use to protect your bananas.

PRONUNCIATION

1 **Look at the underlined vowel sounds. Circle the word which has a different sound.**

a	about	allow	doubt	down	own
b	annoyed	choice	employ	going	join
c	clothes	cope	drove	ghost	love

042 **Listen and check.**

2 **Put the words in the box in the correct column according to the vowel sound.**

~~enjoy~~	~~found~~	~~grow~~	hole	how
know	noise	our	own	point
proud	round	toilet	toy	won't

/ɔɪ/	/aʊ/	/oʊ/
enjoy	*found*	*grow*

043 **Listen and check. Repeat the words.**

LISTENING

1 044 **Cover the listening script and listen to the teacher's story. Number the events (a–h) in the order in which they happened.**

a A girl started crying. ______
b The teacher went to look for the girls. ______
c The principal spoke to Mr. Burr. ______
d A girl left the room. ______
e The teacher realized why the girls had really left the room. ______
f The students began a test. 1
g The teacher returned to the classroom. ______
h The girl's friend went to help her. ______

2 **Look at the script and find expressions which mean the same as the following:**

a I had no idea (*paragraph 1*)
____
b make your life difficult (*paragraph 2*)
____
c I was responsible (*paragraph 2*)
____
d she still hadn't come back (*paragraph 4*)
____
e the only thing to do was (*paragraph 4*)
____
f very well behaved (*paragraph 5*)
____

3 **Find four places in the first paragraph where you can add *that*. The first one has been done for you.**

John Burr, a teacher who works in a Chicago school, was asked about his worst teaching experience.

I think that the worst experience ^that I've ever had was in my first year of teaching, and the kids knew that I didn't have a clue how to control them. I was giving the students a French test, a subject most of them hated. I had a class of eighth graders and these children do anything they can to give you a hard time. It's the age group I find the most difficult.

There was one girl in the class whose mother had died recently. She used to sit there and stare at me, as if it was my fault. And she had a friend who sat next to her, who was probably the biggest trouble-maker in the whole school.

Anyway, one day, the students were taking their test – it was about relative clauses, which we'd just done in class – when this girl started crying. She put up her hand and asked if she could go to the bathroom. I knew that she was probably thinking about her mother, so I said yes. I mean, what else could I do? So she left the room and ten minutes later she still hadn't come back. I was wondering what to do next when her friend put up her hand and asked if she could go and look for her. I couldn't go myself because the students would all cheat, so I said yes, and she left the room, too.

Ten minutes later, there was still no sign of her. I thought there was nothing for me to do but to go and find them both myself. I was coming out of the girls' bathroom – they weren't there – when the principal called me from the other end of the corridor. "Mr. Burr!" he yelled. "Is there any particular reason why your students are all talking to each other in the middle of a test? I suggest that you get back to your classroom immediately."

I ran back to my classroom and there were the two girls, sitting quietly, as good as gold. The rest of the class was also quiet, continuing with their test. It was only when I graded the test that I understood what had happened. The whole class scored more than 80% – the first and last time that ever happened!

11 Age

GRAMMAR

1 Write the words in the correct order to make sentences.

a wish hadn't smoking I started I .

____

b could vacation If go only on I .

____

c told only I had truth the her If .

____

d didn't so homework much I wish have I .

____

e I swim had I to learned wish .

____

f wasn't it wish I raining .

____

2 Write a wish or regret for the sentences below.

a I have so many regrets.
I wish *I didn't have so many regrets.*

b I don't have a lot of money.
I wish ______________________

c I can never find time to read.
I wish ______________________

d I didn't pay attention in class yesterday.
I wish ______________________

e I overslept this morning.
I wish ______________________

f I ate too much for dinner last night.
I wish ______________________

g I'm not good at sports.
I wish ______________________

h I feel anxious all the time.
I wish ______________________

Check (✓) the wishes or regrets that are true for you.

3 Put the verbs in parentheses into the appropriate tense.

a Where *would you live* (you live) if you could live anywhere in the world?

b If you ______________ (not need) to work, what would you do with your life?

c If you could change one thing about your appearance, what ______________ (you change)?

d What ______________ (you say) if you met your favorite movie star?

e If you ______________ (be) invited to a party in Hollywood, what would you wear?

f How would you feel if the government in your country ______________ (change)?

g What would you do if you only ______________ (have) twenty-four hours to live?

h If you had three wishes, what ______________ (they be)?

Write true answers to the questions.

a ______________________

b ______________________

c ______________________

d ______________________

e ______________________

f ______________________

g ______________________

h ______________________

4 Write unreal conditional sentences based on the situations below.

a I don't understand. I can't explain.
If I understood, I would / I'd be able to explain.

b I feel tired. I won't go out tonight.

____

c I'm in love. I think about him all the time.

____

d I'm not a liar. I tell the truth.

____

e I can't dance. I don't go to nightclubs.

____

f I love Coldplay. I buy all their albums.

____

g I have five children. I spend a lot of time cooking.

____

5 **Put the verbs in parentheses into the correct tense.**

a If I had met the right person, I *would have gotten* (get) married.

b If I __________ (go) out more often, I would have met more people.

c I __________ (go) out more often if I had had more time.

d I would have had more time if I __________ (not work) so hard.

e I __________ (not work) so hard if I hadn't needed the money.

f If I had had more money, I __________ (be) more relaxed.

g I __________ (have) more friends if I had been more relaxed.

6 **Complete the sentences so that they are true for you.**

a If I had lived two hundred years ago, I

____

b If my parents had been movie stars, I

____

c If I hadn't studied English, I

____

d If I had been born in the United States, I

____

VOCABULARY

1 **Underline the correct adverb.**

a **A**: Do you have any idea where you are going on vacation this year?
B: Yes, **clearly** / **hopefully** we're going to Tahiti.

b **A**: I bet you're feeling tired.
B: **Actually** / **Unfortunately**, I'm feeling fine.

c **A**: Have you heard any news about Helen recently?
B: Yes, Pete saw her last week. **Apparently** / **Personally**, she decided to quit her job.

d **A**: Did you get tickets for the Rolling Stones?
B: No. **Definitely** / **Predictably**, they sold out on the first day.

e **A**: Philip, what's wrong?
B: I don't know how to say this, but, **basically** / **surprisingly**, I don't want to see you anymore.

f **A**: So you hadn't seen her for twenty years?
B: That's right. But, **obviously** / **unbelievably**, she hadn't changed at all.

g **A**: Did you stay up late last night?
B: Yes. **Fortunately** / **Stupidly**, I didn't have go to work this morning.

2 **Complete the paragraph with appropriate adverbs from the list below.**

I'm (1) __________ getting old. (2) __________, I don't mind having less energy, but I'm very unhappy about the wrinkles. My face is (3) __________ full of lines. (4) __________ something had to be done, so I went shopping for anti-aging cream. I found a cream that promised to make me look ten years younger in a month. I (5) __________ believed it and paid a lot of money. (6) __________, I lost the instructions and I used the cream four times a day. (7) __________, I was only meant to use it once a day. Now my face is bright red and the skin is peeling off. (8) __________ my doctor will be able help me ... and I won't look ten years older!

1 fortunately / positively / definitely
2 Personally / Hopefully / Regularly
3 basically / stupidly / surprisingly
4 Predictably / Clearly / Actually
5 surprisingly / practically / stupidly
6 Fortunately / Unfortunately / Incredibly
7 Apparently / Naturally / Positively
8 Definitely / Honestly / Hopefully

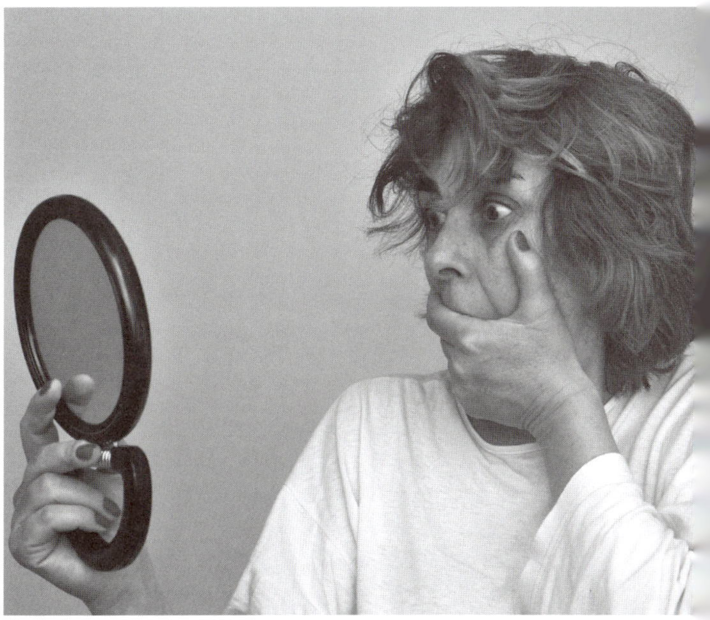

045 **Listen and check.**

3 Write the words in order to make sentences.

a a don't go I lot out .

I don't go out a lot.

b can't drive I well very .

c concerts don't enjoy going I much to very .

d childhood don't I my remember very well .

e a family I lot my see .

f I life live my sensibly very .

g abroad don't go I much very .

h I like loudly rock singing songs very .

Change the sentences to make them true for you.

4 Put the telephone conversations into the correct order.

a Hold on, please. I'll try to put you through ... I'm afraid he's on the other line. Would you like to hold? ___
Oh, hi. Is Tony there, please? ___
Hello. ___
Yes, thank you. ___

b Speaking. Who's calling, please? ___
Good morning. Clyde Interiors. Can I help you? ___
Hello. I'd like to speak to Don, please. ___
This is Miranda, from *Perfect Home* magazine. ___

c Tom, hold on. Can you call me back in five minutes? ___
Joanna? Hi, it's me. ___
Hi, Tom. Listen, I can't talk now. ___
Hello. ___
Just a quick question, OK? What are you doing later? ___

d Certainly. Are you available later on today? ___
Hello. My name is Mike Birdsell. ___
Hello. This is Eva Gomez. Can I help you? ___
Oh, yes, Mr. Birdsell. Thank you for getting back so quickly. We need to have a meeting. ___

046 **Listen and check.**

PRONUNCIATION

1 047 **Listen to two people speaking.**

Which speaker sounds more positive? Which speaker uses a higher tone of voice?

2 048 **Listen to the recording and practice saying the sentences in a positive way.**

a See you tomorrow then.
b I'll look forward to seeing you tomorrow.
c OK, I'll come over around seven.
d I see my family very regularly.
e I'm taking a training course next week.
f I've got something to tell you.

WRITING

Writing a story
Narrative organization

1 **Put the sentences in order to make the first part of a story.**

a I had always wanted to be a photographer, but at first it was hard to find work.

b It happened when I really wasn't expecting it.

c Neither of those was the kind of work that I had dreamed of doing and I was afraid that it would continue like that forever.

d Sometimes, I got jobs taking photographs for websites that sold electrical equipment.

e Then, after two years, I got my first chance of a good picture.

f To begin with, I made my living taking photographs at people's weddings.

1	2	3	4	5	6
a					

2 **Complete the second paragraph using the pictures and notes to help you. Begin like this:**
One day, I was downtown taking pictures ...

old man	running down the street
younger man	running after him
a gun	he looked
I thought	

I put out my foot	younger man
fell over	

older man	ran away	not say anything

You may find the following expressions helpful.

I knew I had to act fast.
I knew I didn't have a second to lose.
As quickly as I could, ...
I was just about to ... when ...
What happened next took me completely by surprise.

3 **Now write the final paragraph. Say what happened next to you, the young man, and the old man. Begin by completing the following sentence:**
If only I had stopped to think, ...

12 Style

GRAMMAR

1 **Insert the adjective in parentheses into the correct place in the sentence.**

a You would look great in a little black dress. (little)

b I can't believe he wears his old jeans to work! (blue)

c I love my leather purse. (Brazilian)

d How many patterned scarfs do you own? (silk)

e He always wears woolen sweaters. (enormous)

f I don't think you should wear an orange top with that long skirt. (purple)

g Not many people look good in shiny gold hot pants, but she does. (leopard-print)

2 **Decide where to put the words on the left in these descriptions of clothes.**

a snakeskin, old — a / an cowboy belt

____

b leather, black — a pair of motorcycle boots

____

c ridiculous, silk — a pair of baggy pants

____

d checked, large — a baseball cap

____

e cotton, brown — a / an old-fashioned shirt

____

f colorful, brand-new — a / an Italian tie

____

g long, plain black — a leather coat

____

3 **Complete the sentences using the structure *have something done*.**

a I didn't sharpen the knife myself. I had it sharpened.

b She doesn't wash her hair herself. She ____________________

c We didn't paint the house ourselves. We ____________________

d They didn't do all the work themselves. They ____________________ by a builder.

e She doesn't design the jewelry herself. She ____________________ by a professional.

f She doesn't color her hair herself. She ____________________ at the hairdresser.

g I haven't whitened my teeth myself. I ____________________ by a dentist.

4 **Read the sentences and underline the most appropriate verb form.**

a I need to **mend my coat / have my coat mended.** Do you know a good tailor?

b My husband **fixed the leak / had the leak fixed**. It took him hours.

c She's **making her wedding dress / having her wedding dress made** and the first fitting is today.

d I'm **cleaning the house / having the house cleaned** tomorrow. I just don't have time to do it myself.

e She **laid new tiles / had new tiles laid** in the kitchen. She did a great job!

f Let's **do our nails / have our nails done** together. We can go to my favorite nail salon.

g Can't you hear the phone ringing? You need to **test your ears / have your ears tested**.

5 Put the words in order to complete the question.

a cut do hair have you your
How often do you have your hair cut ______?

b ears ever had pierced you your
Have ______________________?

c did eyes have last tested you your
When ______________________?

d have home like redecorated to you your
Would ______________________?

e a ever had Have of pair taken pants you
______________________ up?

f do have you your repaired shoes
Where ______________________?

g ever had Have picture taken you your
______________________ by a professional photographer?

6 Write true answers to the questions in Exercise 5.

a ______________________
b ______________________
c ______________________
d ______________________
e ______________________
f ______________________
g ______________________

VOCABULARY

1 Put the words in the box into the correct column.

~~baggy~~	~~belt~~	checked	~~cotton~~
dress	fur	jeans	leather
linen	long-sleeved	low-waisted	wool
pinstriped	plain	scruffy	shirt
silk	snakeskin	stylish	suede
suit	sweater	sweatshirt	top

Clothes	Materials	Adjective to describe clothes
belt	cotton	baggy

2 Look at the pictures and complete the texts with the words in the boxes.

a

Al

deep-set	freckles	mole	receding
sideburns	~~slim~~	streaks	wavy

Al is (1) ___slim___ and has dark, (2) ________ hair with gray (3) ________ and a (4) ________ hairline. He has (5) ________ eyes and long (6) ________. He has (7) ________ and a (8) ________ on his chin.

b

Brad

bald	built	eyeliner	forehead
goatee	mustache	tattoo	

Brad is well (1) ________ and has a (2) ________ on his arm. He is (3) ________ and has lines on his (4) ________. He has a (5) ________ beard and a (6) ________. He wears black (7) ________.

3 Underline the correct alternative.

On Sunday mornings, my husband always (1) **has** / **makes** me a cup of coffee and brings it to me in bed. I (2) **get** / **turn** the radio on and listen to the news before (3) **taking** / **making** a shower and (4) **doing** / **getting** dressed. I don't need to (5) **get** / **make** the children ready for school, so I have time to (6) **do** / **make** my t'ai chi exercises.

My husband likes to (7) **make** / **turn** the TV on and watch it while he's (8) **doing** / **having** a cup of coffee. After that, he does the housework, (9) **getting** / **making** the beds, (10) **doing** / **having** the dishes from the previous night, and so on.

4 Complete the text with the words in the box.

fits	get	go	look	look
match	put	~~try~~	wear	

I hate shopping for clothes. I don't need to (1) try ___ things on, because I know my size – only XXL (2) ___ me these days. I just want to get out of the store as quickly as possible. I always buy dark colors because bright ones don't (3) ___ good on me at all, and I always wear the same kinds of things. The only thing that matters is that I feel comfortable in what I (4) ___. In the mornings, I (5) ___ dressed very fast and (6) ___ on the first pair of jeans that I find. I always wear jeans because they (7) ___ with everything. I can't always find socks that (8) ___, but nobody sees them anyway. I feel sorry for people who worry about what they (9) ___ like. There are more important things in life.

049 Listen and check.

5 Write the missing letters to complete the four mini-conversations.

A: That was very nice of you to give me that hat for my birthday. (1) T h a n k you.

B: You're (2) w _ _ _ _ _ e. My pleasure.

C: What a (3) b _ _ _ _ _ fu_ skirt! It really looks good on you.

D: Do you (4) t _ _ _ k so? Thank you.

E: Thank you so (7) m _ _ h for inviting us. We've had a wonderful few days.

F: Don't (8) m _ _ _ _ _ n it. I'm glad you could come.

G: What a fantastic dinner! That was absolutely (5) d _ _ _ _ _ _ _ s.

H: I'm (6) g _ _ d you enjoyed it. I know you like seafood.

PRONUNCIATION

1 050 Listen to the way the voice rises on each item in a list of words before falling at the end.

He's in his early twenties ↗, tall ↗, dark ↗, good-looking ↗ and rich ↘.

2 051 Listen and repeat the sentences.

a She's slim, elegant, good-looking, and married.
b He's smart, intelligent, attractive, and mine.
c She's got matching shoes, pants, hat, and bag.
d He's wearing a jacket, a belt, boots, jeans, and a T-shirt.

3 052 Listen to the lists below. Are they finished (the voice falls at the end) or unfinished (the voice rises at the end)?

a We have it in a range of colors: blue and green, red and orange, black and white.
b They sell dresses, sweaters and tops, skirts, pants and jeans.
c Which style do you prefer: skinny, low-waisted, tight, or baggy?
d I have wavy hair, a mustache, sideburns, and a beard.

LISTENING

1 053 **Listen to a podcast about fashion designer Ralph Lauren. Check (✓) the main topic of the podcast.**

a his business sense
b his career
c his designs

2 Listen again. According to the show, are the statements true (T) or false (F)?

a Ralph Lauren has stores in different countries. T
b He has financial problems. ______
c He came from a very rich background. ______
d He began selling ties before he left school. ______
e He did not complete his education. ______
f He learned about fashion when he was in the army. ______
g He did not train as a fashion designer. ______
h Lauren's designs were highly fashionable and modern. ______

3 Find the phrases below in the listening script and check (✓) the best explanation.

a *a tale of rags to riches*
☐ a story about becoming wealthy
☐ a story about making money from clothes

b *he's never looked back*
☐ he has never looked at things twice
☐ he has become even more successful

c *that sets him apart*
☐ that was the reason for failing his exams
☐ that makes him special

d *he had a good eye*
☐ he did not need to wear glasses
☐ he had a natural talent for noticing

e *Lauren has it all*
☐ Lauren has everything that anyone could want
☐ Lauren is near the end of his life

Presenter: This week on *Catwalk Talk* we look at one of the biggest names in fashion, Ralph Lauren. Alison Martin, this is a big year for Ralph Lauren, isn't it?

Alison: Absolutely. This year marks the 50th anniversary of one of the most successful fashion houses ever. And Ralph Lauren certainly has good reason to celebrate. He has stores around the world, from Tokyo to Moscow to Milan, and his company is a multi-billion-dollar business.

Presenter: Ralph Lauren is a household name. He must be very rich.

Alison: His own personal wealth is estimated at five billion dollars and he has homes in New York, Colorado, and Jamaica. He also has world-famous collections of vintage automobiles and wristwatches.

Presenter: Was his family wealthy?

Alison: Absolutely not! Lauren's life story is a tale of rags to riches. He was born in New York, the son of immigrants from Belarus, his father a house painter, his mother a pianist.

Presenter: So how did it all begin?

Alison: In high school, he helped to make ends meet by selling ties to his classmates. He left college after two years – before completing his studies – and spent two years in the army. He then worked as a salesman before his career took off.

Presenter: And that was when he opened his first store? I read that he began by selling ties that he'd designed himself.

Alison: Yes, and after that he never looked back.

Presenter: How do you explain his incredible success?

Alison: During his years at college, Lauren studied business, not fashion, and it's this perhaps that set him apart from other fashion designers. There was nothing especially fashionable or modern about his designs, but he had a good eye for clothes, and an even better business sense.

Presenter: Lauren's most famous brands are, of course, Polo and Polo Sport, and his clothes are worn by everyone, from presidents to rappers and boxers.

Alison: Don't forget that Lauren doesn't only sell clothes; he sells a complete lifestyle. You can drink from Ralph Lauren glasses, eat from Lauren plates, and even sleep in Lauren sheets.

Presenter: Now in his seventies, Lauren has it all. He once said that he doesn't want to be too successful ... well, that kind of success would be fine with me!

Notes

Notes

Notes

Notes

Notes